Investigating Geography

FOUNDATION

JACKIE ARUNDALE AND GREG HART

Hodder & Stoughton
www.hodderheadline.co.uk

Acknowledgements

The front cover illustration shows the Eden Project, Cornwall; reproduced courtesy of © Herbie Knott.

The publishers would like to thank the following individuals, institutions and companies for permission to reproduce copyright illustrations in this book(numbers given are figure numbers): Action Plus, 3.7bl; © Adrian Fisk, 4.1, 4.2; AFP Photos, 4.19; Alaska Wilderness League, 1.30; Andrew Ward/Life File, 1.23, 3.7cl, 6.2cl, 6.13cl; AP, 4.4, 6.27, 6.34; © Ashanti Goldfields, 2.2, 2.6, 2.25, 2.26, 2.38; © B & C Alexander, 3.4 (1); B & C Alexander/© Ann Hawthorne, 3.4 (2); © Bettmann/Corbis, 6.25; Lodestone Publishing, 1.8, 3.3; Cape Grim B.A.P.S./Simon Fraser/Science Photo Library, 3.8 (1), 3.8 (5); © Casio, 1.1; © Charles O'Rear/Corbis, 6.5tl; Cliff Threadgold, 6.2br; Corporate Communications Unit, Stoke-on-Trent City Council, 2.20, 2.21; © Craig Aurness/Corbis, 1.25; Digital Stock, p4r; Digital Vision, p28bg; Emma Lee/Life File, 1.22, 3.7tl, 3.7tr, 6.13l; Eyewire, p30 (flags), p94bg; Françoise Sauze/Science Photo Library, 3.8 (2); © Fred Martin, 1.12, 1.26, 1.27, 1.28, 1.34; GE Astro Space/Science Photo Library, 1.3, 1.4; GeoInformation Group, 1.9; Gladstone Museum, Longton, 2.12; Graham Burns/Life File, 6.2tl; © Greg Hart, 4.5, 4.17; Ikon Imaging, p54bg; Ingram Publishing, p6r, 1.32, p30bg, p54bg, p57 (camera, toothbrush); Jeremy Hoare/Life File, 1.10, 6.1tr, 6.1bl, 6.13cr; Jerry Mason/Science Photo Library, 3.8 (6); Jon Woodhouse/Life File, 5.9; Kent News, 6.19r; Landeshauptstadt, Dresden, 2.32; Lionel Moss/Life File, 5.7, 6.2cr; © Mark Edwards/Still Pictures, 6.17; © Crown Copyright, The Met Office, p49tr, 3.10, 3.14; © Michael Busselle/Corbis, 5.27; Mike Arundale, 4.14, 4.21, 4.28, 4.29, 4.30, 5.1, 5.2, 5.3, 5.4, 5.5, 5.13, 5.20; Mike Maidment/Life File, 6.19l; Nicole Sutton/Life File, 3.4 (5); Nigel Shuttleworth/Life File, 6.2tr; PA Photos/EPA, 1.20; © Paul Seheult, Eye Ubiquitous/Corbis, 3.8 (4); Peter Dunkley/Life File, 1.24; Peter Harkin/Life File, 6.1tl; Photoair, 4.25; Photodisc, p4bg, 1.2, p5bl, p7bg, p10b, p12bg, 1.19, 1.33, p44bg, p45r, p45b, p46bg, p48bg, 3.9, p50bg, p52br, p54tl, p54bg, p56bg, p57 (sunglasses, penknife, cars, umbrella) p59br, p60bg, p68bg, p70bg, 4.16, p76bg, 4.22, p86bg, 5.10bg, 5.11bg, p92tr, p93r, p100bg, 5.29, 5.31, p103bg, 6.1br, 6.3, 6.4, 6.5, 6.13r, p113r, 6.35; Richard Powers/Life File, 3.4 (4), 3.22, 6.2bl; © Robert Estall/Corbis, 5.26; © Roger Ressmeyer/Corbis, 5.28; Shell Nigeria Images, 6.32; © Starke Foto Dokument 01099 Dresden, 2.3, 2.4, 2.5, 2.7, 2.9, 2.29, 2.30; Stephen Kraseman/Science Photo Library, 3.8 (3); Sue Cunningham/SCP, 3.4 (2); © Tom Bean/Corbis, 1.29; Tony Craddock/Science Photo Library, 1.17; © US National Park Service, 5.21; Werner Forman Archive/British Museum, 2.10; © Yann Arthus-Bertand/Corbis, 6.5bl (b = bottom; t = top; l = left; r = right; c = centre; bg = background)

The publishers would also like to thank the following for permission to reproduce material in this book: © Bill Bryson. Extracted from *Made in America* by Bill Bryson, published by Black Swan, a division of Transworld Publishers. All rights reserved; © The Guardian for extracts from 'Grim find of 58 bodies …' by Nick Hopkins, Jeevan Vasager, Paul Kelso, Andrew Osborn, Guardian, 20 June 2000; 'Dover no port in a storm' by Vikram Dodd, 28 March 2000; extracts from *Miss Smilla's Feeling for Snow* by Peter Høeg, Harvill, 1993 © Peter Høeg and Munksgaard/Rosinante, Copenhagen, 1992, English translation © Farrar, Straus & Giroux Inc. and The Harvill Press, 1993. Translated from the Danish by F. David. Reproduced by permission of The Harvill Press; extracted information on pages 50 and 52 from The Met Office (see extracts for acknowledgement); © The Observer for extracts from 'Film of the week: "Not one less" by Peter Preston, Observer, 25 June 2000; maps reproduced from Ordnance Survey mapping with the permission of the Controller of Her Majesty's Stationery Office, © Crown copyright, Licence No. 100019872; Trentham Books for the extract from *Visions of the Future: why we need to teach for tomorrow* by D. Hicks and C. Holden (eds), Trentham, 1995; "Diagnostic and Formative Assessment of Student Learning" article by David Leat and Julie McGrane, pages 4-7, January 2000 edition of Teaching Geography.

Every effort has been made to trace and acknowledge ownership of copyright. The publishers will be glad to make suitable arrangements with any copyright holders whom it has not been possible to contact.

Note about the Internet links in the book. The user should be aware that URLs or web addresses change regularly. Every effort has been made to ensure the accuracy of the URLs provided in this book on going to press. It is inevitable, however, that some will change. It is sometimes possible to find a relocated web page, by just typing in the address of the home page for a website in the URL window of your browser.

Orders: please contact Bookpoint Ltd, 130 Milton Park, Abingdon, Oxon OX14 4SB. Telephone: (44) 01235 827720. Fax: (44) 01235 400454. Lines are open from 9.00–6.00, Monday to Saturday, with a 24 hour message answering service. You can also order through our website www.hodderheadline.co.uk.

British Library Cataloguing in Publication Data
A catalogue record for this title is available from the British Library

ISBN 0 340 846348

First Published 2003
Impression number   10 9 8 7 6 5 4 3 2 1
Year   2009 2008 2007 2006 2005 2004 2003

Copyright © 2003 Jackie Arundale and Greg Hart

Cover photo from shows the Eden Project, Cornwall; reproduced courtesy of © Herbie Knott.
Typeset by Fakenham Photosetting Limited, Fakenham, Norfolk.
Printed in Italy for Hodder & Stoughton Educational, a division of Hodder Headline Plc, 338 Euston Road, London NW1 3BH.

Investigating Geography A

Contents

Connecting Places

Where am I?

Am I at the right place?

The wristwatch shows the time and date. However, look again. It also tells you where you are. The display gives figures for your **latitude** and **longitude**. This tells you where you are on any place on earth (see pages 12 and 13).

You can check your **location** using the latitude and longitude of a place in the index of an atlas.

△ **Figure 1.1** The Casio Global Positioning wristwatch.

The Global Positioning System

The watch uses technology called the **Global Positioning System (GPS)**. Aircraft and ships have been using the GPS to find their way for many years.

△ **Figure 1.2** Most ships and aircraft now use the Global Positioning System for navigation

Activities

1 Look at the wristwatch in Figure 1.1. Write down the latitude and longitude. Only write down the first two sets of figures out of the four sets after the N and the E.

2 If you already know how to find places from their latitude and longitude, find the country shown by the figures. You could even find the city.

How does it work?

The Global Positioning System uses satellites and computers to tell you where you are. These satellites can pinpoint places on the Earth. There are 24 of them that orbit the Earth. The GPS needs three satellites to pinpoint where you are. They are about 20 000 km above the Earth.

▷ **Figure 1.3** Receivers get signals from satellites that pinpoint where they are

How satellites link people

People use satellites to talk to each other. Television pictures can also be bounced off satellites. Pictures taken by satellites can be used to find out more about the Earth.

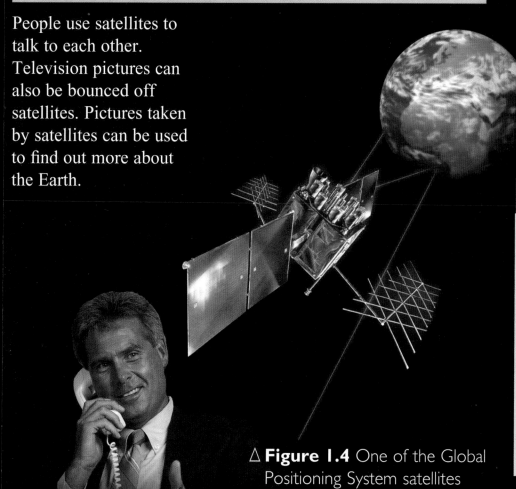

△ **Figure 1.4** One of the Global Positioning System satellites

Activities

3 Draw a diagram with labels to show how the Global Positioning System works. Include:
- at least three satellites
- the Earth
- a GPS receiver that can look like a watch
- lines to show information being sent.

Grids on maps

An **Ordnance Survey** (OS) map has a numbered grid to describe where places are. Lines from the top to the bottom of the map are called **Eastings**. Lines across the map are called **Northings**. You can find a grid square by using a four-figure **grid reference**. You can pinpoint a place in a square by using a six-figure grid reference.

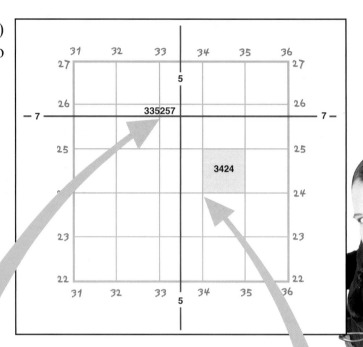

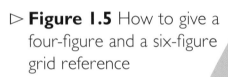

▷ **Figure 1.5** How to give a four-figure and a six-figure grid reference

› Reminder – using a six-figure grid reference

1 Find the first two figures of the four-figure reference, e.g. 33.
2 Work out how far the point is away from the next Easting line, e.g. towards line 34. Think of it as nine invisible lines so that line 5 is half way across the square. Write the figure, e.g. 335.
3 Find the second set of numbers of the four-figure reference, e.g. 25.
4 Work out how far the point is up from the next Northing line, e.g. towards 26. Think of it as nine invisible lines across the map. A bit more than half way could be 7, e.g. at 257.
5 The full six-figure grid reference for the point would then be 335257.

› Reminder – using a four-figure grid reference

1 Find the line to the left side of the square (the Easting).
2 Look along the top or bottom of the map to find the two figures for this line. Write down the two figures, e.g. 34.
3 Find the line along the bottom of the square (the Northing).
4 Look along the right or left side of the map to find the two figures for this line, e.g. 24. Write these two figures after the first two figures to give the four-figure grid reference for the square, e.g. 3424.

How big is my place?

You can measure the **distance** between places from a map by using the map scale. For example, a scale of 1:50 000 means that one centimetre on the map represents 50 000 centimetres or half a kilometre on the ground.

Scale can be used to measure the size or **area**. By measuring the length and width you can work out how big the area is.

For example, the area of the football pitch (Figure 1.6) is 50 × 100 m or 5 000 square metres.

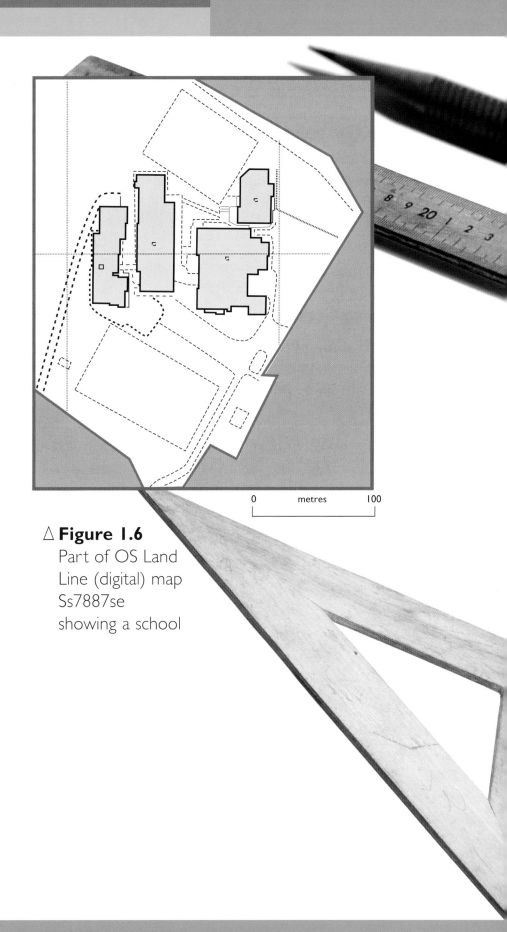

0   metres   100

△ **Figure 1.6**
Part of OS Land Line (digital) map Ss7887se showing a school

Activities

1 **a** Find out the names of the primary schools in your local area.
b Locate these on a copy of a local OS map.
c Give their grid references.
d Measure the distance from each primary school to your secondary school.

What's at my place?

What features make a place?

Every place is different. Each is made up of natural and human features. A steep slope or a river could be part of its natural landscape. This is also called its **physical geography**. Houses and roads are built by people so they are part of the **human geography**.

What can you see by looking down?

A map is a plan of an area and shows some detail. An Ordnance Survey 1:50 000 map shows the physical geography and how people use the area. How people use the area is called **land use**.

Vertical air photos show more details of a place, for example, land use. A vertical air photo is clear enough to show all the buildings, roads, woods and fields.

Towns and cities are called **urban** areas. The land use is mostly housing. In other places, the land use can be a mixture of houses, factories and open areas. The most open areas are in the countryside. These areas are called **rural** areas. Some of this land is farmland.

ICT activity

Use the Multimap web site to find maps of the area where you live: www.multimap.com If you live in a large urban or rural area, you can also find a vertical air photo. You may be able to see your house.

▽ **Figure 1.8** A school is often shown on an OS map by writing Sch, but this is not always done

▽ **Figure 1.7** An OS 1:50 000 scale map of part of east Bristol. There is a school at 634745. It is not marked because the map is too crowded at that point

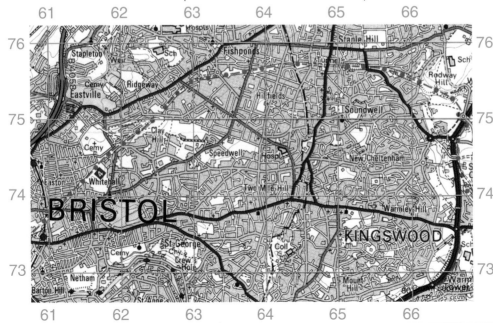

Is it good to live there?

The word **environment** is used to describe the features of an area. There are good and poor features in an environment. People make changes to their environment. Some changes can make it more attractive to live there, others make it worse.

△ **Figure 1.9** A vertical air photo of part of east Bristrol. The school is at 634745 on the OS map

Location of the vertical air photo.

Activities

1 Look at the map in Figure 1.7. Is this an urban or rural area? Give one reason for your answer from the map.

2 Write a list of the main types of land use either in your local area or the area around the school shown in Figure 1.9. This list may help you to start:

- houses
- factories
- roads.

3 Write down three questions you might want to ask someone about living in your local area. Ask at least one person your questions. Write up their answers. Do you agree with their answers?

How can I describe a place?

Writing about a place

Writing about a place is one way to record its geography.

You should:
• use accurate information
• include statistics (figures)
• include information you have researched

Then:
• organise it into paragraphs
• use special geographical words

To:
• describe the physical and human features
• include reasons to explain what you have described

You can include statistics in your description in several ways:
• in the writing itself
• in a table
• as a graph

△ **Figure 1.10** An oblique air view of part of the central part of London

Activities

1 Look at the photograph (Figure 1.10) or a view out of your classroom window. Write a geographical description of the place.

2 Practise **line drawings** using photos in books or magazines. Better still, practise by drawing a field sketch.

Sketching a scene

Drawing a **field sketch** of a place is another way to record its geography. To draw a field sketch, follow these steps:
- Begin with a frame to outline the scene you want to draw.
- Draw the the skyline and main slopes.
- Add the details you want to include, using simple lines and shading.
- Print labels on or around the sketch.

▽ **Figure 1.12** The coastline at Lulworth Cove in Dorset

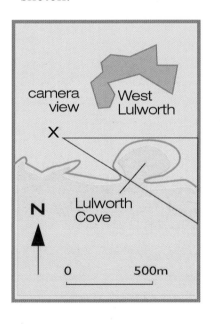

△ **Figure 1.11** Map of the scene shown in the photo. The photo was taken at point X looking east between the red lines

▷ **Figure 1.13** A line drawing of the coastline at Lulworth Cove, Dorset. The sketch can be completed with shading or colours

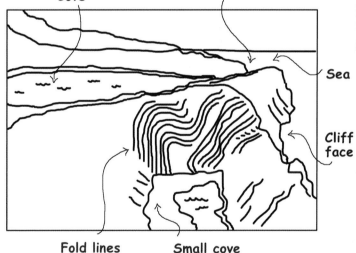

ICT
activity

Make a line drawing of a digital photo.
- Insert photo from file into Word
- Click on Draw tools
- Click on Line from menu
- Draw lines along main features
- Delete the photo
- Add labels, either as a text box or callout
- Select Group from the menu to save as an image

How can I find other places?

What is latitude and longitude?

To find a place on a world map, you would use a grid. The Earth is a **globe** so you cannot draw a simple grid of squares on it. Mapmakers draw a world map by using a **map projection**. This makes it easier to draw a flat map. The grid is made up of latitude and longitude. Lines of latitude go from east to west. Lines of longitude go north to south.

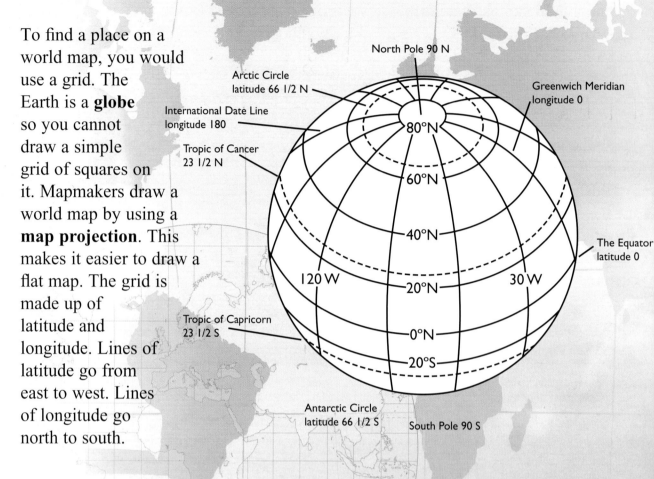

△ **Figure 1.14** The main lines of latitude and longitude

▽ **Figure 1.15** An equal area projection map of the world with lines of latitude and longitude

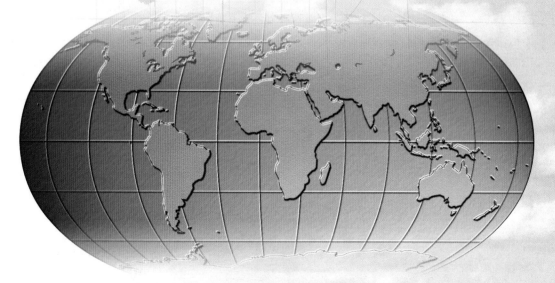

How does latitude and longitude help find a place?

The **Equator** is a line of latitude drawn around the widest part of the globe. It is at latitude 0.

Any place not on the Equator is either north or south of this line of latitude.

The **Greenwich Meridian** is a line of longitude drawn from the North Pole to the South Pole. It is at longitude 0.

Any places not on the Greenwich Meridian are either east or west of it.

The Greenwich Meridian passes through London.

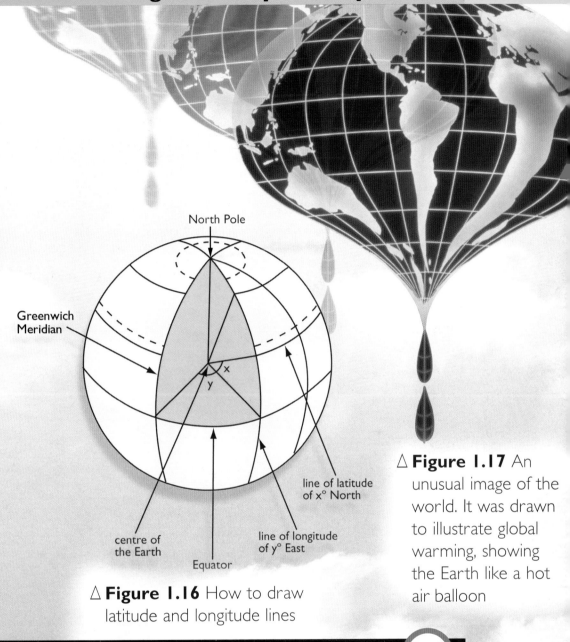

△ **Figure 1.16** How to draw latitude and longitude lines

△ **Figure 1.17** An unusual image of the world. It was drawn to illustrate global warming, showing the Earth like a hot air balloon

Activities

1 In an atlas, look up the latitude and longitude for the place where you live, or the nearest town or city that is listed in the index of an atlas.

- New York
- Calcutta
- Cairo
- Lima

2 For each of these places, write down their figures for latitude and longitude:

3 Describe how lines of latitude and longitude have been drawn on some atlas maps. See if they curve.

Where am I linked to?

Global links

The Internet is a system that links people anywhere on the Earth using a computer. Distance between places is not a problem.

▽ **Figure 1.20** A cybercafe in Cambodia where you can send emails, search the World Wide Web, and have a drink

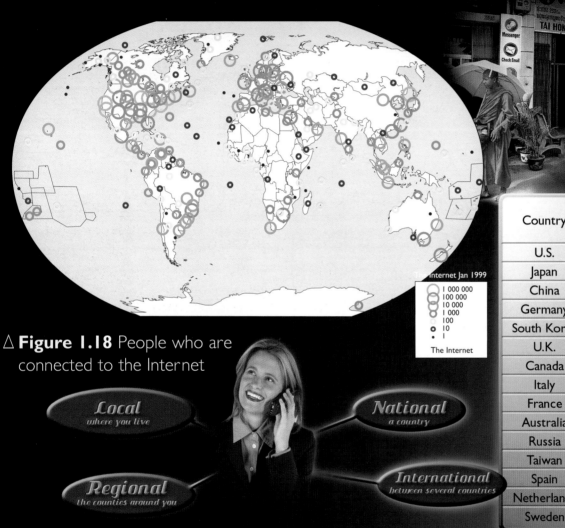

The Internet Jan 1999

◯	1 000 000
◯	100 000
◯	10 000
◯	1 000
◦	100
◦	10
·	1

The Internet

△ **Figure 1.18** People who are connected to the Internet

Local where you live

National a country

Regional the counties around you

International between several countries

△ **Figure 1.19** The calls I make to people

Links with other places

In your own home, there are many examples of foods and objects from other places. Some come from different parts of this country. Other goods come from other countries. Many cars you see were made in different countries. Water, electricity and food have come from other places.

▽ **Figure 1.20** A cybercafe in Cambodia where you can send emails, search the World Wide Web, and have a drink

Country	Internet users (millions)	Population in millions
U.S.	134.6	288
Japan	33.9	127
China	22.5	1307
Germany	19.9	82
South Korea	19.0	47
U.K.	16.8	59
Canada	15.4	31
Italy	12.5	58
France	9.0	59
Australia	7.6	20
Russia	7.5	143
Taiwan	7.0	23
Spain	5.6	41
Netherlands	5.5	16
Sweden	4.4	9

△ **Figure 1.21** The top 15 countries for Internet use

Is it good to have links?

It takes energy to move people and goods around the world on trains, lorries, ships and planes. This traffic can cause air pollution. One airport has asked passengers to pay extra for their flight. This money will help pay for the damage that aircraft do to the environment. As trade increases between countries, the more pollution there will be.

▽ **Figure 1.22** A holiday in Barbados

▽ **Figure 1.23** People who live near airports suffer from aircraft noise

ICT activity

Aircraft fuel causes air pollution. Trees can soak up some of the pollution.

www.futureforests.com/ calculators/flightcalculator shop.asp This website calculates the amount of CO_2 produced by a flight and how many trees will be lost.

Luton airport is planning to take care of the environment. Use the website to find out more about Luton Airport's plans.

www.london-luton.com

Try other websites to find out what they are doing about pollution.

Activities

1 Look at the map (Figure 1.18) showing where people are linked to the Internet. Which areas have the most links? Suggest a reason why.

2 List five items that you own that were made in a different country.

3 Choose one of the items. Which country did it come from?

4 How does each item help you in your daily life?

What questions can I ask?

What's the same and what's different?

Not all places are the same. Some do have similar features. However, many are very different from each other. If you **compare** places, you can see how they are similar or different.

To help describe places, you should use geographical words. However, a word used in geography can mean something different in another subject. You should describe a fact using an adjective. An adjective is a describing word, for example, a *steep* hill, a *wide* river or *dirty* factory.

A statistic will help give a piece of information. For example, the river is *10 m* wide, there are *23* cars parked, or *5 000* people live here.

▽ **Figure 1.25** The River Thames in London

Headings to compare places	Examples of words
Relief (shape of the land)	plains, valley, hill
Drainage (rivers)	stream, river, tributary
Climate and weather	hurricane, clouds, pressure
Vegetation	forest, grassland, crops
Population	densely populated, multi-racial, migration
Work	industry, farming, services
Recreation and leisure	park, leisure centre, stadium
Transport	airport, motorway, navigation

▽ **Figure 1.24** Goosekill Bridge, Castleton, Derbyshire

big	low
wide	narrow
rough	gentle
large	small
steep	high
smooth	deep

△ Adjectives

A **geographical enquiry** is a way to find out something in geography. This is when you find out about a topic or question. You then write it up. Information can be collected by visiting a place. This is called fieldwork. You can also find information from reference books and the World Wide Web.

What questions will I ask?

Speech bubbles in figure:
- What is the land used for?
- Is the landscape changing?
- Have these trees been planted?
- How did this valley get its shape?
- What natural features are in this landscape?
- How busy is this road?
- Is it good to have all these people here?
- Why have these people come here?
- Where have these people come from?

△ **Figure 1.26** A scene in the UK Lake District **National Park**

› The steps for a geographical enquiry

1 Ask a question; for example, which is the best road to live in?
2 List the facts you will need; for example, house prices or street survey.
3 What else do you need to find out; for example, people's views?
4 How can you find this out; for example, by **fieldwork** or survey?
5 Collect and record your findings.
6 Present your findings as writing, maps, sketch or graphs.
7 Answer the question you first asked.

Figure 1.27 A student doing fieldwork

Activities

1 Write four things about Figure 1.24 by completing these sentences:
- This is a picture of a river in …
- The river is …
- The buildings are …
- This place is a …

Use the same sentences to describe Figure 1.25.

2 You can compare Figure 1.25 with 1.24 by completing these sentences:
- The river in London is …
- The buildings in London are …
- Castleton is a …

3 List ten adjectives that can be used to describe your local area.

4 Write five sentences that describe your local area.

5 Use an atlas to find out these facts about the UK:
- the highest mountain
- the longest river
- the biggest city.

6 Plan a survey of where pupils in your class live.

Use the steps for an enquiry to plan what you have to do.

Include:
- A survey
- A map
- A graph

Is information always right?

Is it the truth?

The pictures show a holiday resort called Portinatx. It is on the Spanish island of Ibiza. The extract describes what Portinatx is like. However, how accurate is this information?

Sometimes the information is only partly true. The person who wrote it is trying to persuade you to visit Portinatx. This information is likely to be **biased**. Even a photo may not show the whole truth. The information about this holiday resort may have left out some important facts about the area.

Activities

1. List five good things about Portinatx.

2. Suggest three bad things about Portinatx.

Figure 1.28
Portinatx

◁ The beach

▷ New holiday villas being built

18 see ibiza

Portinatx

The bay offers wonderful panoramic views, crystal-clear water, high rocky shorelines and a seabed of fine, white sand. The amazing views of this beautiful bay are a wonderful combination of diamond bright, clear sea reflected in many shades of blue. There is a games centre with bowling and pool tables. There are music bars, pubs and an active nightlife scene.

– Information from a website advertising a holiday in Spain.

How can I check the information?

It is important to check the information about a place. To do this, find out who wrote it and why they wrote it. Check the information from one source with information from another source. The World Wide Web can be one good source of information, but it has a special problem. Anyone can set up a website and put anything on it. You have to be sure that the information you use is right.

△ A tourist shop and holiday flats

〉 What to check

- When was it written? Is the information out of date?
- Who wrote it? Have they been there?
- Why was it written? Does the writer want to persuade you?

▷ A street in Portinatx

Activities

3 Would you like to have a holiday in Portinatx? Suggest a reason for your answer.

4 Design a poster to advertise your town as a holiday resort. Make sure that you are biased. Include some doubtful facts about your town.

5 Now design a very honest poster about your town as a holiday resort.

6 Which poster would you use to promote your town as a holiday resort?

▷ **Figure 1.29** The logo of the Alaska Wilderness League. This is an organisation that wants to conserve the environment in the area as it is: www.alaskawild.org/

△ **Figure 1.30** The environment in the Arctic National Wildlife Refuge in Alaska

2   see **alaska**

ICT activity

1 Log on to www.alaskawild.org to find out more about the Arctic National Wildlife Refuge.

2 From the home page, click on 'Learn more about the Arctic National Wildlife Refuge'.

3 From the next screen, find the contents, then click on 'Take a visual tour of the Arctic region'.

4 Explore the other parts of this website.

5 Design a website that would give the oil companies' point of view.

▷ **Figure 1.31** This text was adapted from information from the Alaskan Wilderness League

The Arctic National Wildlife Refuge

The Arctic National Wildlife Refuge is the last five percent of the northern coast where there is no oil exploration. The Arctic National Wildlife Refuge is a protected arctic landscape. It is the crown jewel of America's National Parks. Many oil companies want to drill for oil in this area. This refuge is in danger of being destroyed by those looking for oil beneath the fragile arctic landscape.

Assessment tasks

Background

You work for a company called Image Makers. The company helps to plan and advertise leisure and recreation facilities. The district council in your area wants to improve the leisure and recreation facilities for people who live in the area. They have given your company the job of doing this.

Before you begin this task, you should decide if you are going to work:
• by yourself
• as a pair
• as a team with the work divided between you.
(Your teacher will help you to make these decisions).

△ **Figure 1.32** The Image Makers' Company

How to write your report

The report should be set out in four parts. You should add your own ideas in every part.

A: The planning background
This part gives background information about the area to help plan the kind of leisure and recreation facilities that people will want to use.

B: Existing facilities and access
This part aims to describe the facilities there now and how to get to them.

C: Publicity
In this part, you will provide ideas about how to advertise the facilities.

D: New ideas
This section is where you can present some ideas for new facilities or how to change what is already there.

Tasks

A: The planning background
- Give information about the total population, land use and how the area has changed.
- Give some views about what people might want.
- The information can be presented as short descriptions, tables of figures or basic graphs.

B: Existing facilities and access
- Give a list of the different types of leisure and recreation facilities. Divide them into indoor and outdoor facilities.
- Give brief details of what can be done at each facility listed.
- Give information about how people might get to some of the facilities. This could include bus routes, footpaths and car parks.
- Mark the facilities on a map. You could use four-figure grid references to locate the facilities.
- Write some notes to describe the pattern of facilities in the area.

C: Publicity
- Make a leaflet or short brochure to advertise the facilities.
- Think of a slogan that would draw attention to the facilities.
- Include some sketches or photos of some of the facilities.

D: New Ideas
- Give at least one idea for a new leisure and recreation facility for the area. You could think about whether the area's physical geography can be used, for example if there is a river. There could be a new swimming pool or a historic trail.
- Give reasons why it might be successful.

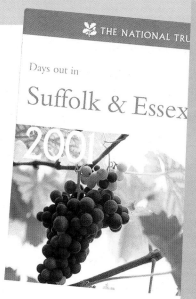

places to visit

Review

What have I learnt in this section?

In this section, you have learnt about three main things:

- How to study places to see what is there and to think about some ways in which places are linked.
- How to use maps and photographs to find out about where places are and what is there.
- How to ask geographical questions and develop some of the skills required to research the information you need to answer those questions.

Activities

1 Which is the odd one out from these lists? Use an atlas to find out. Explain your answers.

List A
England
London
Wales
Scotland

List B
Bristol
Sheffield
Wales
Norwich

List C
Severn
Trent
Danube
Thames

2 Find the latitude and longitude of each of these places:
- Athens
- Berlin
- Madrid
- Paris
- Vienna

3 Study the photograph (Figure 1.33).
a Make a line drawing of it. Add labels to point to the physical and human features that you can identify.
b Write down at least three questions that you might want to ask about the scene. The questions can be about the physical geography, the human geography or a question about the environment.

4 Does the place where you live or a place near to it have a twin town? If it does, use your research skills to find out some ways that the twin town is similar and some ways that it is different to where you live. If not, you can choose a place yourself or your teacher can choose for you. Find out about:
- the people who live there
- what its position is, if it is near the sea, inland, in mountains or plains
- the name of the biggest river that flows through it
- what people do for a living
- what people might do for recreation

△ **Figure 1.33** A scene in South West England

You can find some of the answers in an atlas. For more information, use reference books, CD-Roms and the World Wide Web.

Development: Change in Contrasting Localities

Change for the better?

What do you think?

△ **Figure 2.1** A concept map of trade

Activities

1 Study Figure 2.1. Use a dictionary and find out the meanings of these important words.

2 What do you know about these places?

Ghana   Germany   England

3 Compare your ideas with other people in your class.

a Which were the same?
b Which were different?
c Make a tally chart to record the class views.
d Show your results as a bar chart.
e What was surprising, interesting, or unusual about the results?

4 Look at the photos on page 25.

△ **Figure 2.2**

△ **Figure 2.3**

△ **Figure 2.4**

△ **Figure 2.5**

△ **Figure 2.6**

△ **Figure 2.7**

Activities

5 Suggest three words to describe each photograph.

6 There are two photos from Germany, two from Ghana, and two from England. Which two photos go together for each place?

7 Choose one photograph and write a sentence about it. For example,

'*Figure 2.2 is in ......*

The photograph shows ......'

So what about these places?

Key
people/sq.km

0 - 10
10 - 50
50 - 100
100 - 200
200 - 500
500 - 1000
1000 - 2500
no data

0   3000km

△ **Figure 2.8** World
population density, 1996

▽ **Figure 2.12**
Plate produced
by the Stoke-on-
Trent potteries
now in the
Gladstone
Museum, Long

Development –
A shorthand definition

Development is about
people

Development is about
people making
choices based on
values

Development
is about
people making
choices based on
values about the
quality of life.

△ **Figure 2.11**

△ **Figure 2.9** Nordbad
swimming pool, restored as
part of a development
project in the Ausere
region of Dresden

▷ **Figure 2.10** Gold
produced from Ghanaian
gold mines, including Obuasi,
in the Ashanti region

Investigating choices

This chapter is about local development. Local means a small area. It can be in a town or countryside. A lot happens in a **local area**. Figure 2.8 locates the three local areas this chapter will look at. They are Obuasi, Stoke and Ausere. Each is somebody else's local area.

Development is an important theme in geography. It describes peoples' views about living there. Development is not always easy to measure. But we can say how well people live, what people think about where they live, and show they care for their environment.

'Quality of life' is about whether people have basic needs. This includes clean water, enough food, shelter and healthcare. In the UK we have a good quality of life. This is not so for many poorer countries.

Choices and places

People make choices that can change other people's lives and change where they live. In Obuasi, Ausere and Stoke, decisions and plans have changed these areas. Changes can be good for an area. Sometimes they cause new problems. How have these changes affected the people who live there? How might they have affected you?

Activities

1 Look at page 26. What can you buy from Stoke, Obuasi and Dresden?

2 If you bought gold from Obuasi, how would that decision affect the people who live there? Use the heads and tails to explain the effect of your decision.

Heads	Tails
I bought gold to	earn a living.
This will help me to	make jewellery.
Miners in Obuasi will	have money to spend on basic needs.
The miners' families	have more work.

3 a Use Figure 2.8 and an atlas to help you to complete the table above.

Local area	Country	People/sq km	Continent
Obuasi			
Stoke			
Ausere			

b Use your completed table to help you to correct the following paragraph:

*Ghana is on the **continent** of **America/Africa**. It is a **smaller/larger** continent than Europe. England and Germany has a population density of **200–500/10–50** per square kilometre. This is **higher/lower** than Ghana.*

What does quality of life mean?

'Quality of life' means how well the people live in a given place. Not everyone has the same quality of life. Some may have very similar lives to you, others very different. There are a number of reasons for these differences. These include access to food, water, shelter and healthcare, the right to have a good job and the right to a safe environment where we live.

Quality of life depends on how much money we have. Richer countries are able to provide the basic needs for its people. We need to improve the quality of life for many people in poorer countries. There is enough money and skill in the world, but decisions have to be taken on how to share these resources for all.

Development projects

Development projects are one way to help. These can improve people's quality of life. But how do they improve it? In Ghana 42%, in Germany 16%, and in England 19% of the population are under 15. The box below lists some of the concerns of these people about their future quality of life.

Young people's concerns for the future

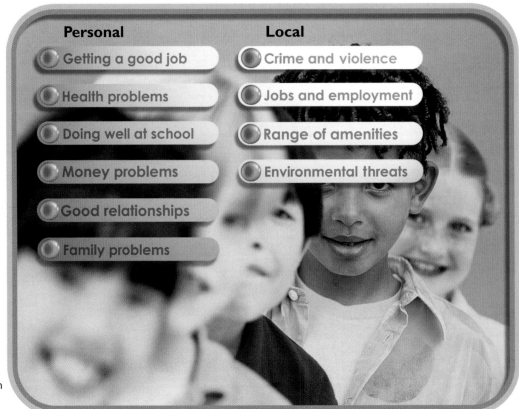

Personal
- Getting a good job
- Health problems
- Doing well at school
- Money problems
- Good relationships
- Family problems

Local
- Crime and violence
- Jobs and employment
- Range of amenities
- Environmental threats

Source; Hicks, D & Holden, C (eds), **Visions of the Future, Why We Need to Teach for Tomorrow**, Stoke on Trent, Trentham

▷ **Figure 2.13**
Quality of Life frame

Getting a good job

Health problems

Doing well at school

Environmental threats

Money problems

Quality of life in a locality My name ... Place ...

Range of amenities

Good relationships

Crime & violence

Family problems

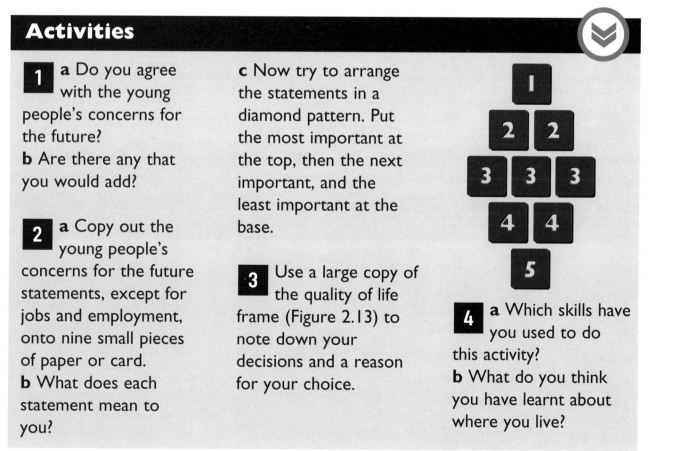

Activities

1 **a** Do you agree with the young people's concerns for the future?
b Are there any that you would add?

2 **a** Copy out the young people's concerns for the future statements, except for jobs and employment, onto nine small pieces of paper or card.
b What does each statement mean to you?

c Now try to arrange the statements in a diamond pattern. Put the most important at the top, then the next important, and the least important at the base.

3 Use a large copy of the quality of life frame (Figure 2.13) to note down your decisions and a reason for your choice.

4 **a** Which skills have you used to do this activity?
b What do you think you have learnt about where you live?

So what about values and geography?

All of us have our own set of views. These are our *values* and beliefs. Some of these come from other people, our family, our friends, and ideas from television. Some of our views are to do with our own character.

We think differently about other places. What people think of other places is a difficult area for geographers to investigate. You are going to do this by thinking about where you live and your feelings about other places.

Scale

A local area is part of a region, and part of a nation. Individual people live in each of these places. For example, individuals live in Obuasi, which is part of the Ashanti region of Ghana. Information about an individual is at the personal **scale**. But most of the information about a country is at a **national** scale. Using this information helps us to develop our own personal views and values about places.

▽ **Figure 2.14** Table to show **communications** data

Country	1990 Main telephone lines per 1 000 people	1998 Main telephone lines per 1 000 people	1990 Mobile phone subscribers per 1 000 people	1998 Mobile phone subscribers per 1 000 people	1990 Television per 1 000 people	1998 Television per 1 000 people	1990 Personal Computers per 1 000 people	1998 Personal Computers per 1 000 people
United Kingdom	441	556	19	252	433	645	108	263
Germany	441	567	4	170	525	580	91	305
Ghana	3	8	0	1	15	115	0	2

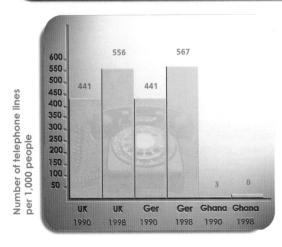

◁ **Figure 2.15** A bar chart to show main telephone lines per 1 000 people

Activities

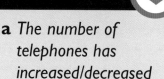

Look at the data in Figure 2.14. This tells you about the number of telephones, mobile phones, televisions and computers there are in the UK, Germany and Ghana.

1 Figure 2.15 shows a bar chart for telephones using the information from Figure 2.14. There are two bars for each country, the first is for 1990 and the second for 1998.

a Has the number of telephones increased or decreased in these countries between 1990 and 1998?

b Which country had the most telephones in 1998?

c Which country had the fewest telephones in 1998?

d Which country would it be easy to make a telephone call in?

e Which country would it be difficult to make a telephone call in?

2 On graph paper, draw a bar chart similar to Figure 2.15 to show the number of mobile phone subscribers in the United Kingdom, Germany and Ghana in 1990 and 1998.

3 Choose another way to show the number of personal computers for each country.
These graphs show how good the communication is in each country. They also show how access to communications has changed between 1990 and 1998.

4 Use Figure 2.14 to complete these statements about the UK.

a *The number of telephones has increased/decreased from ...... to ......*

b *The number of mobile phones has increased/decreased from ...... to ......*

c *The number of televisions has increased/decreased from ...... to ......*

d *The number of computers has increased/decreased from ...... to ......*

5 Use Figure 2.14 to write similar sentences about Ghana.

6 Suggest why school children in the UK might know more about the world they live in than a child from Ghana.

Activities

On the next pages, you will find information about three development projects. Pages 34 and 35 show how the Ceramic Quarter in Stoke was changed. Pages 36 and 37 show how the gold mines in Obuasi were improved. Finally, pages 38 and 39 show why a new swimming pool in Ausere was built.

1 Your task is to investigate these development projects. To do this you will need a strategy. A strategy is a planned way or the steps needed to work on a task. An important part of this strategy is making simple notes about each development project. Below is an example for the Ceramic Quarter in Stoke:

Step 1: Read information on pages 34–5. Make sure you look at the maps.

Step 2: List down any words you do not understand. Check these with your teacher.

Step 3: On a copy of the information on pages 34–5 underline important pieces of information or facts using crayons. This is a text analysis.

Where?: Where is the Ceramic Quarter?

What?: What is the Ceramic Quarter project about?

Why?: Why was the project necessary?

When?: When did work begin and end?

How?: How was the project carried out?

Benefits (fact file): What has changed for local people?

Step 4: You have highlighted the main points about the Ceramic Quarter Project. Read through to check you only have the important points.

Step 5: Using your text analysis you can write a case study. Use the layout in Figure 2.16 to help you. You can also add a map to locate the place.

2 Use the same strategy to write a case study for Obuasi, Ghana and for Ausere, Germany.

Activities

Where:	• Longton • South of Stoke • A traditional ceramic area
What?:	• Redevelop the area • New jobs • Design and arts centre • Conserve the history
Why?:	• Decay and pollution • Poor quality of life • Unemployment
When?:	• Started in January 1992 • Ended in 1995
How?:	
Benefits:	

◁ **Figure 2.16** You can complete the last two: How? and Benefits.

3 Figure 2.17 compares each development project. On a copy, use your case notes to complete columns 1, 2 and 3. Put a tick if you think the project will improve the area but a X if it makes things worse for the people.

▽ **Figure 2.17** How development has changed Obuasi, Stoke-on-Trent and Ausere

4 Complete column 4 by writing in what are the similar effects of the three development projects.

5 Complete column 5 by writing in what are the different effects of the three development projects.

6 Do you think that these projects have been good for these areas? Suggest a reason for your answer.

How has the development helped to change.........	1. Obuasi	2. Stoke-on-Trent	3. Ausere	4. What I think is similar	5. What I think is different
the chances of getting a good job					
the health of the people who live there					
how much money people have					
the environment					
how people feel about living there					

Is this development of a local area?

The Ceramics Quarter, Stoke-on-Trent

› Where?

The project was in Longton in the south of the city of Stoke-on-Trent. It was an old industrial area. The area had many ceramics factories.

› What?

The project was funded by the European **Regional** Development Fund. The project aimed to:

- **redevelop** an historic industrial area
- build a new ceramic design centre
- provide training
- conserve the areas' industrial heritage
- attract industry back to the area
- attract tourists to the area

› Why?

During the last 150 years, coal mining, clay extraction, iron and steel works, pottery waste tips and widespread pollution had changed the city's **landscape**.

This caused problems:

- a poor image of the area
- a poor environment
- **congestion** and pollution
- people living there had a poor quality of life
- the area depended on ceramics for work
- high unemployment – particularly in the ceramics industry.

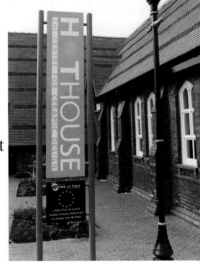

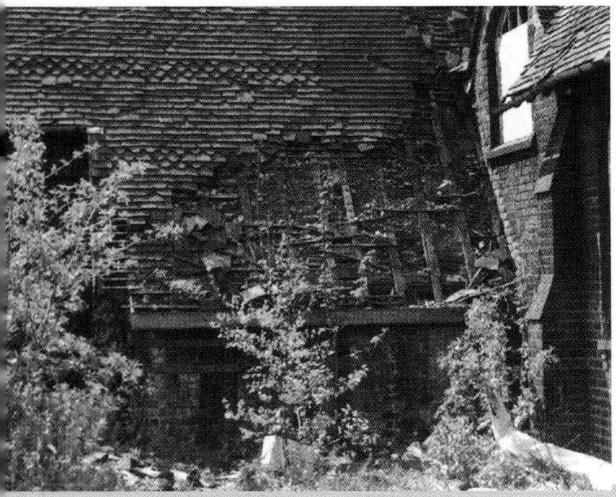

› When?

The work started in January 1992. The first phase finished in 1995. Another phase will finish by 2010.

› How?

The project's actions involved:

- Renovating and converting an old school building into a ceramic design centre called the 'Hothouse'. The Hothouse will use technology to help the ceramics industry. There will be workshops, industrial design and computers and a kiln room.
- Converting a vacant industrial building to craft workshops for artists.
- Improving the Gladstone Pottery Museum as a major tourist attraction.
- Improving the fronts of local buildings and landscaping.
- Running a training centre with Staffordshire Training and Enterprise Council to help find employment in building and environmental work.

△ **Figure 2.19** The Hothouse design centre

◁ **Figure 2.18** Neglected St James's School building, Longton, Stoke-on-Trent

FACT FILE: THE CERAMICS QUARTER, LONGTON

The number of jobs in the pottery industry has fallen from 55 000 in 1962 to 18 600 in 1995

The Ceramics Quarter project was successful in generating employment.

52 jobs have been created.

164 jobs have been safeguarded.

81 businesses have received help with accommodation.

Raised profile of the city of Stoke-on-Trent in Europe.

Increased visitor numbers to the Gladstone Pottery Museum from 35 000 to 50 000 per year.

ICT links

Some useful websites:

www.thisisstaffordshire.co.uk

www.inforegio.org/urban/upp/ src/Bullet05.htm

www.stoke.gov.uk

▽ **Figure 2.20** Outline map of Britain

△ **Figure 2.21** Staffordshire, with Stoke-on-Trent

▽ **Figure 2.22** An OS extract showing Longton and the Ceramics Quarter Explorer 258 1: 25 000

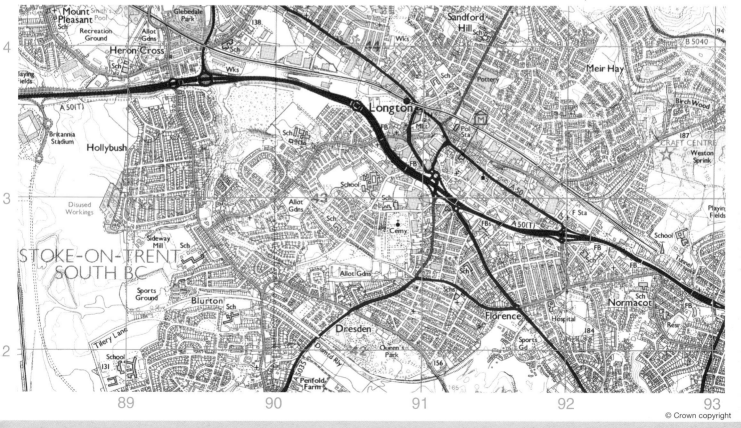

© Crown copyright

Is this development of a local area?

Obuasi, Ashanti Goldfield, Ghana

› Where?
Obuasi is in the Ashanti region of Ghana. It is 200 km northwest of Accra.

› What?
The Obuasi gold mine is owned by The Ashanti Goldfields Company (AGC) and the Ghanaian government. Mining began in 1897. Gold is a scarce resource. It is expensive to mine. In one tonne of rock, there is 4 grams of gold. Governments use gold as reserves of 'money'. Mining in Obuasi has caused environmental destruction.

△ **Figure 2.23** Overview of the Obusai mine, Central Ghana

› Why?
Gold mining in Obuasi damaged the environment. Arsenic, sulphur and dust from the roasting process polluted the air. Open-cast mining destroyed the landscape and killed the plants.

Cyanide and poisonous deposits polluted the water. Fish died or were poisonous to eat. The villagers' water supply was poisoned. It was 30 km downstream before the water was safe to use.

› When?
In 1990 an environmental policy was planned.

› How?
A new factory now safely removes the arsenic from the gold extraction process. New laboratories monitor the workers' health, the air and water quality. Safety at work polices have reduced accidents. Landfill sites for rubbish, and water for dampening dust have helped with the local facilities.

Tube wells provide clean water supplies for the villages. Schools, market stalls and street lighting have been improved.

◁ **Figure 2.24** A truck at Ashanti Goldfields

Estimates suggest that there is at least 20 million ounces of gold available to be mined at Obuasi.

Ashanti gold mine's production rate puts it in the world's top ten.

There has been a long history of mining in Ashanti.

Gold output from Obuasi is between 550 000 and 650 000 oz per year. The cash cost of production is US$223/oz (1999).

Within the Obuasi township AGC has provided 15 boreholes with handpumps to improve water supply.

In 1999, 743 111 oz of gold were produced in Obuasi.

ICT links

Some useful websites are:

www.mining-technology.com/projects/Obuasi/index.html

www.moles.org/ProjectUnderground/reports/goldpack/goldpack_f.html

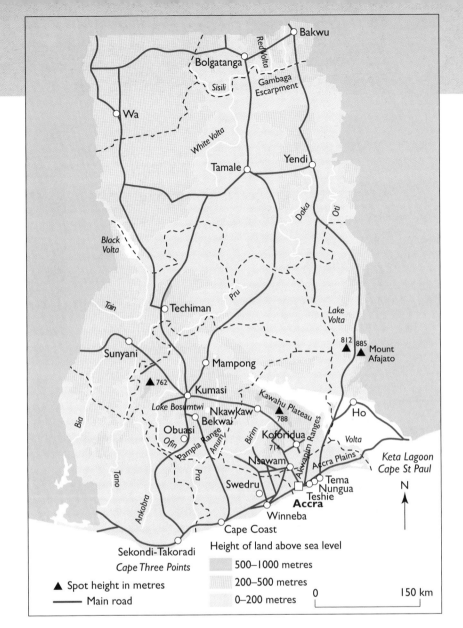

△ **Figure 2.25** Map of Ghana

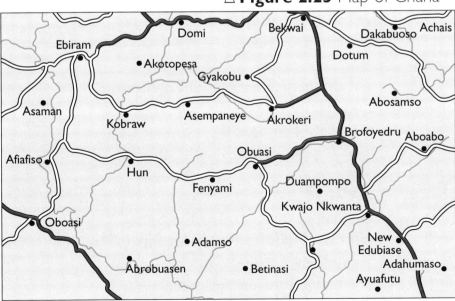

△ **Figure 2.26** Map showing Obuasi

› Where?

Dresden is in Saxony in South East Germany. The Nordbad swimming baths are located in the centre of the Ausere Neustadt (outer new town).

› What?

Ausere Neustadt is an area of poor housing. 65% of the houses did not have a bath or a shower. Unemployment in the area was 20%.

△ **Figure 2.28** Solar roof-top collectors o buildings surrounding the Nordbad

The European Regional Development Fund paid for the Nordbad project. It rebuilt the 19th-century swimming baths. The project encouraged other redevelopment in the area. Unemployed people could get job training. The project helped to improve the local **economy** and boost house values.

△ **Figure 2.27** Nordbad swimming pool in operation, 1997

The project gave a sense of **community** amongst local residents. The residents' association ensured the views of local people were included in the project.

› Why?

The baths opened in 1896 to provide **sanitary facilities** for the local people. Many houses then did not have a bath. The baths were a meeting place. It became a ruin due to lack of investment.

› When?

The project started in the 1990s.

› How?

Pedestrian access to the baths was difficult. Several buildings were demolished to give pedestrian access. Around the baths, buildings and their surroundings were improved. A children's playground, sun-bathing lawn and fountain area was built. The aim was to make the Nordbad complex a community centre for health, social and recreational activities.

There were training opportunities for young unemployed people to specialise in the restoration of listed buidlings.

The Nordbad swimming pool has an adjustable floor for variable water depths, a children's pool, sauna, physiotherapy units and cleansing baths. Local schools use the pool for lessons.

The Nordbad now provides bathing for the 12 000 local residents and the rest of the city.

During the first half of 1997, 30 000 people visited the baths.

The 24 companies employed for the work had to employ and train young unemployed people.

37 unemployed people were given jobs.

17 trainees gained building qualifications.

20% of all housing in the area has been modified.

△ **Figure 2.29** Map of Germany

CT
inks

A useful website:

www.inforegio.org/urban/upp/src.Bullet08.htm

△ **Figure 2.30** Aerial view of area surrounding Nordbad

Assessment tasks

There is nowhere the same as the place that you live. All places are different. The developments studied in Ausere, Obuasi or Stoke describe a small part of what those places are like.

Many people who live and work in these places will have different views about the same place. You have studied the specific changes in these towns, but there are also other changes taking place.

So is this the full story?

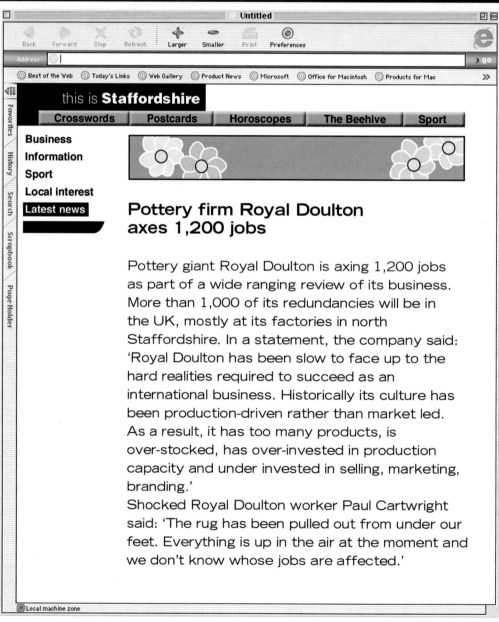

this is **Staffordshire**

| Crosswords | Postcards | Horoscopes | The Beehive | Sport |

Business
Information
Sport
Local interest
Latest news

Pottery firm Royal Doulton axes 1,200 jobs

Pottery giant Royal Doulton is axing 1,200 jobs as part of a wide ranging review of its business. More than 1,000 of its redundancies will be in the UK, mostly at its factories in north Staffordshire. In a statement, the company said: 'Royal Doulton has been slow to face up to the hard realities required to succeed as an international business. Historically its culture has been production-driven rather than market led. As a result, it has too many products, is over-stocked, has over-invested in production capacity and under invested in selling, marketing, branding.'
Shocked Royal Doulton worker Paul Cartwright said: 'The rug has been pulled out from under our feet. Everything is up in the air at the moment and we don't know whose jobs are affected.'

△ **Figure 2.31** An Internet search shows what is happening to Stoke and to Royal Doulton worker, Paul Cartwright

Tasks

1 What do you understand by the terms:
Choices   Quality of Life   Values.

Use a copy of the writing frame below to help you plan your answer.

Development Terms	I think this means	For example	I also think it means	For example	Finally I think.....
Quality of Life					
Choices					
Values					

2 The Ceramics Quarter Project in Stoke aimed to improve the Longton area.

a What do you think were the aims of this project?
b Why was this important for this area?

The Ceramics Quarter Project	I think has improved	For example	I also think it has improved	For example	Finally I think.....
Quality of Life					
Choices					
Values					

3 How has the Ceramics Quarter project improved people's lives in that area?
Write a sentence to describe how peoples' choices and quality of life changed.
Use a copy of the writing frame below to help you plan your answer.

Tasks

4 With your teacher read Figure 2.31 which is about Paul Cartwright who lives in Stoke. Discuss with your teacher any words or ideas you do not understand.

5 Use the futures frames on this page to describe:

a Paul Cartwright's current position
b what you might think his future position could be in 10 years time
c what you think his probable future will be in 10 years time.

6 To make Paul Cartwright's preferred future into his probable future, what actions would need to be taken?

7 Describe a possible development project that could improve Paul Cartwright's quality of life, using the headings:

- Where?
- What?
- Why?
- When?
- How?

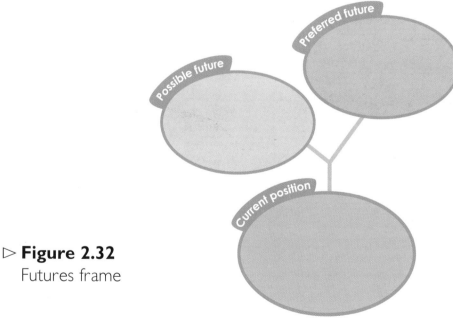

▷ **Figure 2.32**
Futures frame

Review

So how have you developed?

Activities

▷ **Figure 2.33** Water sampling at Obuasi

1. Look back at the ideas that you produced at the start of the unit. This was how you answered question 1 on page 24. What other ideas could you add to your original answer? Either write a new set of ideas to show what you now know, or add in a different colour to your original answer.

2. What surprises you, or interests you, about what you have learnt?

3. Look at the photo (Figure 2.33) and the sketch (Figure 2.34). This is a way to show information about an area. Using these as a guide, choose a photo from this unit. Draw an outline sketch of the photo and annotate to show what you now know about that place.

4. Make a list of the skills you have used in this unit. Underline any that you think are geography specific. Underline in a different colour any that you think that you might use again.

5. Would you like to add to or alter the shorthand definition of development on page 26?

▷ **Figure 2.34** Annotated sketch of water sampling at Obuasi

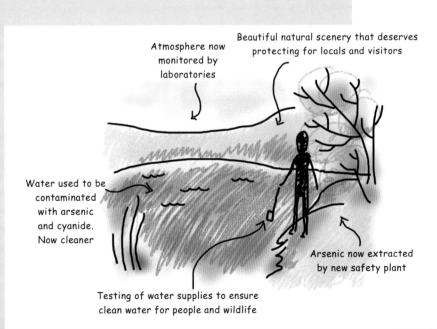

Atmosphere now monitored by laboratories

Beautiful natural scenery that deserves protecting for locals and visitors

Water used to be contaminated with arsenic and cyanide. Now cleaner

Arsenic now extracted by new safety plant

Testing of water supplies to ensure clean water for people and wildlife

How is the weather described in books?

I have respect for the Danish winter. The cold – not what is measured on a thermometer, but what you can actually feel – depends more on the force of the wind and the relative humidity in the air that on the actual temperature ... When the first clammy rain showers begin slapping me and November in the face with a wet towel, I meet them with fur-lined capucines, black alpaca leggings, a long Scottish skirt, a sweater and a black waterproof cape.

◁ From **Miss Smilla's Feeling for Snow**
by Peter Hoeg

▷ **Figure 3.1** Images of weather from fiction

This morning when I set off it was −19°F (−28°C) ... Unless you have a particularly vivid imagination, or are reading this in a chest freezer, you may find such extreme chilliness difficult to conceive ... When you step outside in such weather, for the first instant it is star-tlingly invigorating – not unlike the experience of diving into cold water ... Your face feels as it would after a sharp slap, your extremities are aching and every breath you take hurts.

▽ From **Seasons of the Wind**
by Janice Bowers

△ From **Notes from a Big Country**
by Bill Bryson

Gusts of wind buffeted the truck as we pulled to a stop ... We put up our tent as quickly as possible, but even with the tent, refuge eluded us that night. For hours we lay in our sleeping bags listening to the wind. Whirling through the pass ... it roared like traffic on a distant freeway as it rushed towards the dunes ... Gravel rasped across the ground cloth, and sand sifted through the mosquito netting. Morning finally came but brought no respite from the wind, which still blew cold and steady from the south east.

Activities

1 With your teacher read each of the extracts. Which book sounds most interesting? Give a reason.

2 Make a list of the adjectives used here to describe the weather.

3 Draw a front cover for one of the books to show the weather described by the author.

How does the weather affect you and me?

Weather means the day-to-day changes in the **atmosphere** for a particular place, e.g. temperature, **precipitation**, wind speed.

Climate means the average weather conditions for a particular area.

Does the weather affect me in the playground?

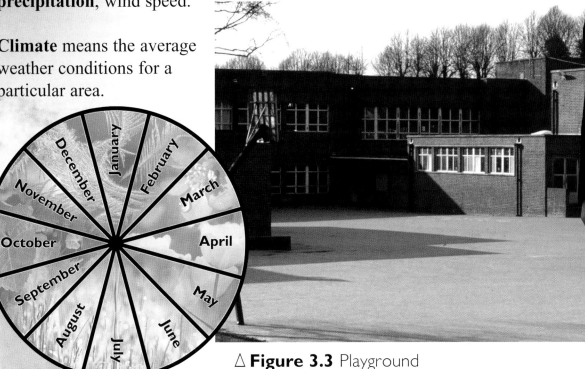

△ **Figure 3.3** Playground

△ **Figure 3.2** Calendar

Activities

4 Which season are you most likely to:

- eat ice cream
- kick leaves as you walk along the pavement
- be off school with the flu
- wear wellington boots
- throw snowballs at a friend
- play in the back garden
- wear sun-tan cream
- dry clothes on a washing line
- have a picnic
- scrape ice off the car windscreen
- wear shorts
- take an umbrella with you

5 Look at Figure 3.3, then think about your school. Plot on a map where you would put the things below and give a reason for each choice.
- benches for pupils to sit in the sun
- trees to give shelter from the wind
- benches for pupils who want to sit in the shade
- a washing line to dry the art aprons
- a greenhouse to grow tomatoes.

How does the weather affect me and you?

▽ **Figure 3.4** Photographs of (1) an Inuit
(2) Peruvian (3) Antarctic Researchers
(4) **Nomad**
(5) Me

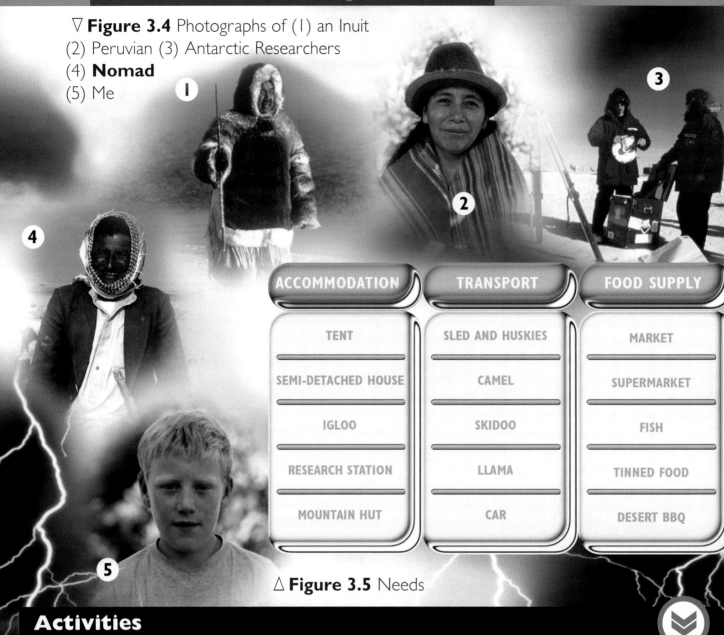

ACCOMMODATION	TRANSPORT	FOOD SUPPLY
TENT	SLED AND HUSKIES	MARKET
SEMI-DETACHED HOUSE	CAMEL	SUPERMARKET
IGLOO	SKIDOO	FISH
RESEARCH STATION	LLAMA	TINNED FOOD
MOUNTAIN HUT	CAR	DESERT BBQ

△ **Figure 3.5** Needs

Activities

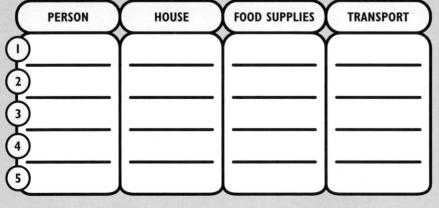

PERSON	HOUSE	FOOD SUPPLIES	TRANSPORT
1			
2			
3			
4			
5			

△ **Figure 3.6** Choices table

1 Copy out the table, Figure 3.6, and then match up each person with the house, food and transport they are most likely to have.

2 Talk with a partner about how you made up your mind.

Who needs to know what tomorrow's weather will be? Why?

We need time to grit the roads overnight before the ice or snow settles. We need to keep the roads clear for people travelling to work and school the next day.

Frost and rain can affect the setting of mortar and cement.

I clean as many windows as I can when it is dry. I can go weeks without earning money if there are a lot of downpours.

If there is a lot of rain, we need to stop the tennis. Then we cover the courts

△ **Figure 3.7** Why I need to know about the weather

Some people are paid to measure and record weather – they are called **meteorologists**. Many people need meteorologists, including:

• the government
• television and radio stations
• airports
• farms
• insurance companies.

Activities

3 Read through the ways weather affects people's jobs. How might the following people be affected by the weather?
• fire fighter
• ice cream seller
• farmer
• supermarket

How do we measure and record weather?

▽ **Figure 3.8** Weather instruments

1 Rain gauge

2 Wind vane

3 Anemometer

Stevenson screen (5)

Barometer (4)

6 Minimum/Maximum thermometer

Activities

1 Match the pictures with the following descriptions:

- This piece of equipment measures the coldest hours and the warmest temperatures each day.
- A metal container that collects rainwater. At the end of each 24-hour period the water is tipped out into a measuring cylinder.
- A piece of equipment which has cups that are caught by the wind and spin. The speed of the cups tells us the speed of the wind using a scale.
- This container provides protection for the measuring instruments. It allows air to circulate inside.
- This piece of equipment may look like a clock but its dial moves according to the weight of the air.

The World **Meteorological** Organisation checks weather forecasting all over the world. It began in the UK in 1854. In the early days it provided a service to ships, warning of wind conditions and **sea currents**. Now over 2 000 people work for the Met Office in the UK and abroad.

▽ **Figure 3.9** The work of the Met Office

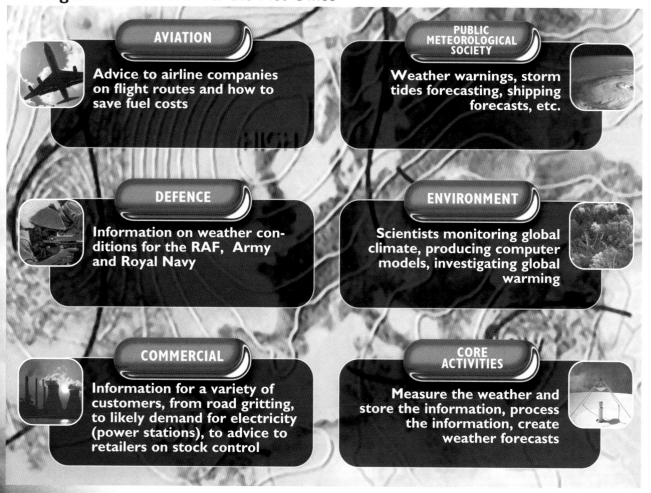

AVIATION
Advice to airline companies on flight routes and how to save fuel costs

PUBLIC METEOROLOGICAL SOCIETY
Weather warnings, storm tides forecasting, shipping forecasts, etc.

DEFENCE
Information on weather conditions for the RAF, Army and Royal Navy

ENVIRONMENT
Scientists monitoring global climate, producing computer models, investigating global warming

COMMERCIAL
Information for a variety of customers, from road gritting, to likely demand for electricity (power stations), to advice to retailers on stock control

CORE ACTIVITIES
Measure the weather and store the information, process the information, create weather forecasts

Activities

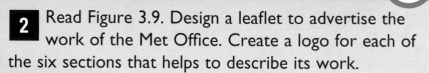

2 Read Figure 3.9. Design a leaflet to advertise the work of the Met Office. Create a logo for each of the six sections that helps to describe its work.

How do we measure and record weather?

Weather maps

Weather maps are used to show: temperature, precipitation, wind speed, wind direction and cloud cover.

The special symbols on a weather map are called the **synoptic code**. Figure 3.10 shows the weather conditions for most of Europe on one day in July.

The synoptic symbols (Figure 3.11) are used to show information for a single weather station. In Figure 3.12, the symbols show that the wind is blowing from the north-east at speeds of between 23 and 27 knots. The sky is ⅞ covered by cloud. Rain is falling. The temperature is 4° C.

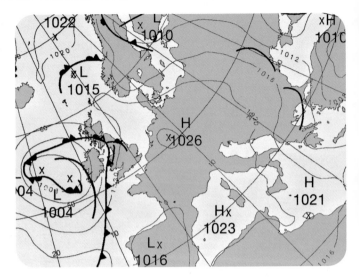

△ **Figure 3.10** A weather map for the UK on 31 July 2000 (Information supplied by the Met Office)

◄ ▷ ▽ Synoptic Symbols

WIND

Speed (knots)	Symbol	Speed (knots)	Symbol
Less than 1	◎	33-37	
1-2	—○	38-42	
3-7	—○	43-47	
8-12	—○	48-52	
13-17	—○	53-57	
18-22	—○	58-62	
23-27	—○	98-102	
28-32	—○	103-107	

The arrow from the weather station symbol shows the direction from which the wind is blowing. The feathers on the end of the arrow tells us how fast the wind is blowing. Each half feather is 5 knots

PRECIPITATION

	Symbol		Symbol
Rain	●	Fog	≡
Drizzle	،	Thunderstorm	↯
Shower	▽	Hail	▲
Snow	✳		

TEMPERATURE
This is given in degrees Celsius. The number is written on the left of the weather station symbol.

△ **Figure 3.11** The synoptic code (Information supplied by the Met Office)

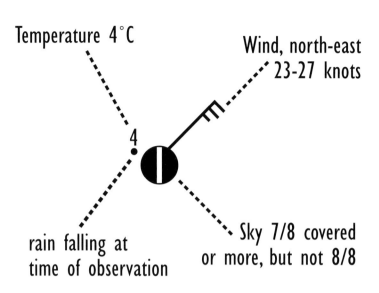

Temperature 4°C

Wind, north-east 23-27 knots

4

rain falling at time of observation

Sky 7/8 covered or more, but not 8/8

△ **Figure 3.12** A weather station

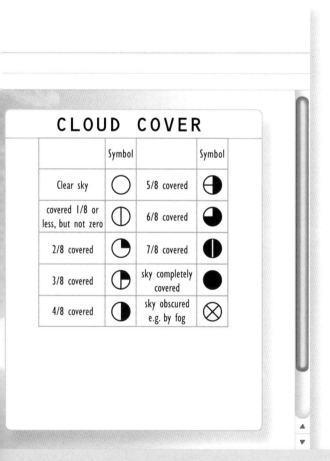

CLOUD COVER

	Symbol		Symbol
Clear sky	○	5/8 covered	◑
covered 1/8 or less, but not zero	◔	6/8 covered	◕
2/8 covered	◔	7/8 covered	◖
3/8 covered	◔	sky completely covered	●
4/8 covered	◑	sky obscured e.g. by fog	⊗

1 Using the information about the synoptic code, describe the weather conditions for two of the sets of symbols below in Figure 3.13.

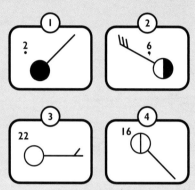

△ **Figure 3.13** Weather stations

2 Draw the symbols you would use to show the following weather conditions:

a Wind from the north; speed 48–52 knots. Temperature 3° C. Hail is falling and the sky ⅝ covered by cloud.

b Wind from the south-east; speed less than 1 knot. Temperature 27°C. No precipitation and clear skies.

3 Cut a local or UK weather map out of a newspaper. Describe the weather shown on that day.

How do we predict the weather?

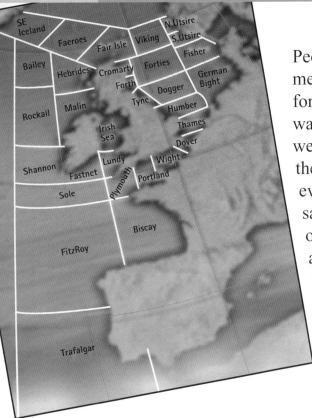

△ **Figure 3.14** Shipping Forecast areas

People have been measuring the weather for over 2 000 years. It was not until 1853 that weather was recorded the same way everywhere to help sailors. Even today, one of the most accurate weather forecasts available is the Shipping Forecast.

NOW THE SHIPPING FORECAST ISSUED BY THE MET. OFFICE AT 11.30 ON SATURDAY 14 JULY 2001 THE AREA FORECASTS FOR THE NEXT 24 HOURS

SOUTH UTSIRE
VARIABLE 3 BECOMING NORTHERLY 4. SHOWERS. GOOD

FORTIES
NORTHEASTERLY BACKING NORTHWESTERLY 3 OR 4, OCCASIONALLY 5. RAIN OR SHOWERS. MODERATE OR GOOD

CROMARTY FORTH TYNE
NORTHEASTERLY BACKING NORTHWESTERLY 3 OR 4, OCCASIONALLY 5 AT FIRST IN TYNE. RAIN OR SHOWERS. MODERATE OR GOOD

HUMBER
VARIABLE 3 BECOMING WESTERLY 4 OCCASIONALLY 5. SHOWERS. GOOD

THAMES DOVER
SOUTHWESTERLY, VEERING NORTHWESTERLY FOR A TIME, 3 OR 4. SHOWERS. GOOD

△ **Figure 3.15** Shipping Forecast, 14 July 2001 (Information supplied by the Met Office)

Activities

1 Listen to a tape of the shipping forecast or use Figure 3.15 and follow it on a copy of the map (Figure 3.14) Make a note of either the wind speed or the wind direction in one section of the map.

2 '*Dover: Mainly a southwesterly wind, will change to a northwesterly wind for a time, wind speed is 3 or 4 on the* **Beaufort scale**, *which is 12–28 km per hour so litter and hair will be blown about. There will be some showers.*'

Read this description. Imagine you were on a ferry. Write an account of your journey or draw a picture to illustrate it.

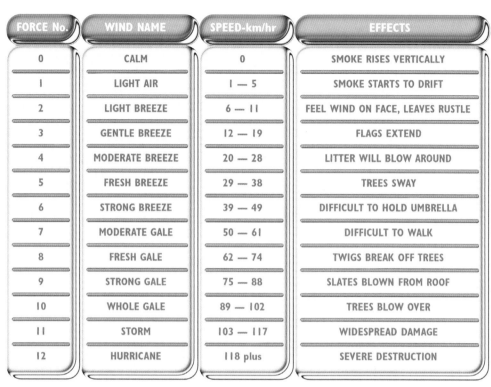

FORCE No.	WIND NAME	SPEED-km/hr	EFFECTS
0	CALM	0	SMOKE RISES VERTICALLY
1	LIGHT AIR	1 — 5	SMOKE STARTS TO DRIFT
2	LIGHT BREEZE	6 — 11	FEEL WIND ON FACE, LEAVES RUSTLE
3	GENTLE BREEZE	12 — 19	FLAGS EXTEND
4	MODERATE BREEZE	20 — 28	LITTER WILL BLOW AROUND
5	FRESH BREEZE	29 — 38	TREES SWAY
6	STRONG BREEZE	39 — 49	DIFFICULT TO HOLD UMBRELLA
7	MODERATE GALE	50 — 61	DIFFICULT TO WALK
8	FRESH GALE	62 — 74	TWIGS BREAK OFF TREES
9	STRONG GALE	75 — 88	SLATES BLOWN FROM ROOF
10	WHOLE GALE	89 — 102	TREES BLOW OVER
11	STORM	103 — 117	WIDESPREAD DAMAGE
12	HURRICANE	118 plus	SEVERE DESTRUCTION

△ **Figure 3.16** Beaufort wind scale

Wind direction can be plotted on a **wind rose** diagram (Figure 3.17). This helps us to spot patterns.

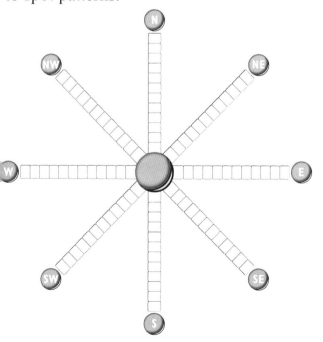

△ **Figure 3.17** Wind rose diagram

> **Stages of drawing a Wind Rose**

1 Draw an 8-point compass.
2 Label the 8 compass points.
3 For each windy day fill in a box on the correct compass axis.

DATE	DIRECTION	FORCE
1	WEST	2
2	WEST	3
3	SOUTH WEST	1
4	SOUTH WEST	1
5	SOUTH WEST	1
6		0
7		0
8	NORTH	3
9	NORTH	3
10	EAST	4
11	NORTH	5
12		0
13	WEST	1
14	SOUTH WEST	2
15	WEST	1
16		0
17	SOUTH EAST	2
18	SOUTH EAST	2
19	EAST	3
20	EAST	3
21	NORTH	3
22	NORTH	2
23	NORTH EAST	2
24	NORTH EAST	1
25		0
26		0
27		0
28	WEST	1
29	WEST	1
30	WEST	1

△ **Figure 3.18** Wind data
A school has collected the wind information for the month of April (Figure 3.18).

Activities

3 Have a go at drawing a wind rose by using information provided by your teacher, or the data for April in Figure 3.18.

4 Use the Beaufort wind scale (Figure 3.16) to keep a record of wind speed for a week.

Climate

The average weather conditions (climate) are worked out by studying all the weather records over a long time. Knowing the climate of an area is very useful. This information helps farmers to decide which crops to grow.

Atlases show the main world climate regions based on rainfall and temperature. They use colours to show the different climates.

Activities

Using an atlas, find a world climate map.

1. How many different climate groups are shown?

2. What is the climate group for the UK?

3. How many climate groups are in a large country, like Australia?

Climate graphs

Geographers use **climate graphs** (Figures 3.19) to show the average monthly temperatures and rainfall for a place in a year.

- The temperature is shown by a line graph.
- Each cross is placed in the middle of the space for each month.
- Each cross tells you the average temperature for that month.
- The crosses are joined together to make a line graph.
- The range is the difference between the lowest and highest monthly temperatures, e.g. the highest temperature is 20°C and the lowest temperature is 16°C. Therefore, the range is 4°C.
- The rainfall is shown by a bar graph.
- Each bar tells you the total rainfall for each month.
- All the monthly totals added together gives the annual rainfall total.

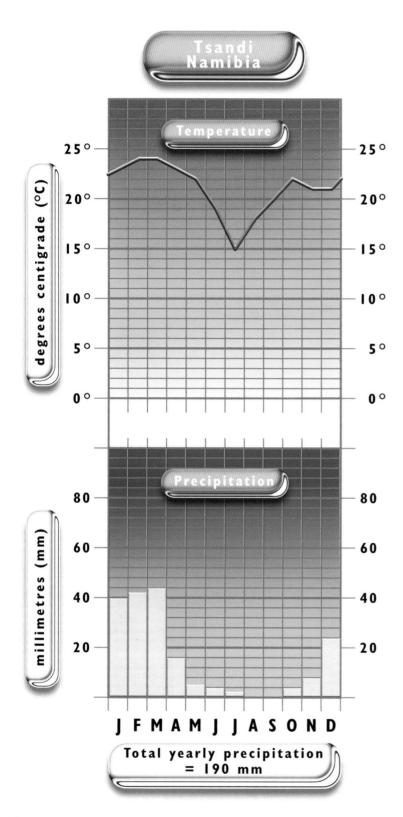

Tsandi
Namibia

Temperature

degrees centigrade (°C)

25° — 25°
20° — 20°
15° — 15°
10° — 10°
5° — 5°
0° — 0°

Precipitation

millimetres (mm)

80 — 80
60 — 60
40 — 40
20 — 20

J F M A M J J A S O N D

Total yearly precipitation
= 190 mm

△ **Figure 3.19** Climate graph for Tsandi in Namibia

Activities

Study the climate graph, Figure 3.19, and then answer the following questions:

4 Which is the hottest month? What is its temperature?

5 Which is the coldest month? What is its temperature?

6 What is the **temperature range** for Tsandi?

7 Which is the wettest month? How much rain fell in this month?

8 Which is the driest month? How much rain fell in this month?

9 Areas with less than 250 mm rainfall for the whole year are **desert**. What is the total annual rainfall for Tsandi? Is Tsandi in a desert area?

Climate

They've won the lottery!

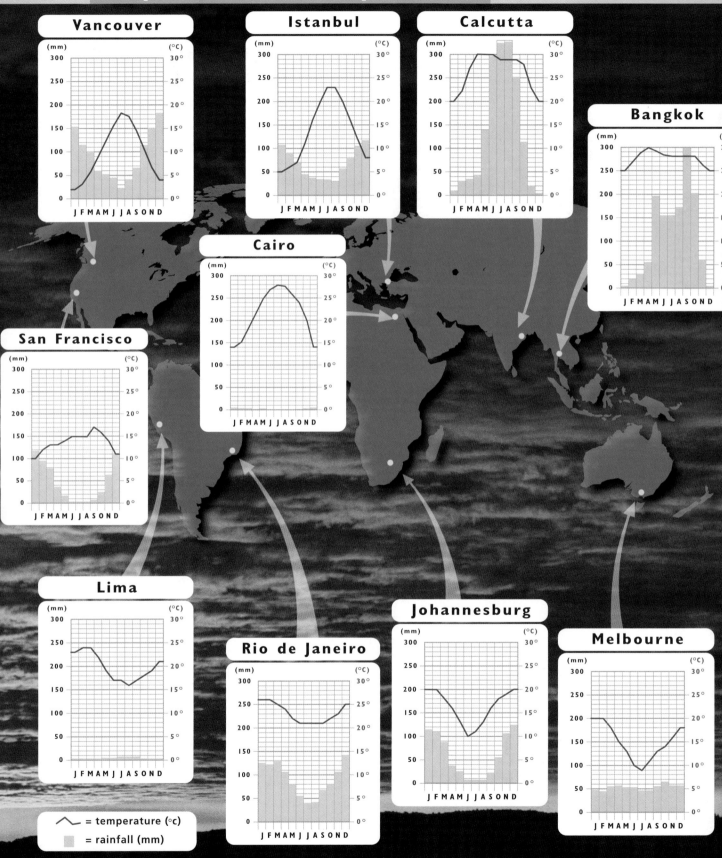

△ **Figure 3.20** Climate graphs for ten cities across the world

MALARIA TABLETS
WATER BOTTLE
MONEY BELT
SUNGLASSES
SOCKS
CAMERA
SWISS ARMY KNIFE
SWIMSUIT/TRUNKS
PACK OF CARDS
DEODORANT
HAIR GEL/SPRAY
PERFUME/AFTERSHAVE
UNDERWEAR
UMBRELLA
SHIRT/BLOUSE
MOUNTAIN KIT
SARONG
SANDALS
MOSQUITO NET
SHORTS
T-SHIRT
THERMALS
MAKE UP BAG
BOOK
RAINCOAT
WASHING KIT (SOAP/TOOTHBRUSH)
SHEET & SLEEPING BAG
LONG SKIRT
TOWEL
JOGGING BOTTOMS
SUN-TAN LOTION
SHAMPOO & CONDITIONER
DRESS
SMART TROUSERS
HAIRDRYER
ROLL MAT
FLEECE
JEANS
SMART SHOES
JUMPER
TRAINERS
TRAVEL GUIDE
WALKING BOOTS
BOOGIE BOARD

Activities

Imagine your family has won the lottery.

1 **a** Choose one of the cities that you would like to visit in Figure 3.20.

b Find a photo from a holiday brochure, the Internet, etc. that will show the climate in that place.

c Label the photo with details about the climate and use it to make a group display for your classroom.

2 Suggest two reasons why you would like to go on holiday to the city you have chosen.

3 Choose five items from the list in Figure 3.21 that you think you would need to take because of the climate. Explain your choices.

4 **a** You're starting in England. What order would you visit the cities on Figure 3.20 so that you would not be experiencing strong climate change?

b Explain your order.

◁ **Figure 3.21** What to pack?

Looking at patterns

Microclimates

Earlier in this chapter (page 45), we looked at how parts of your school and playground might have different conditions. For example, some areas are windier or hotter than others. These changes in climate, in a small area, are called **microclimates**.

Microclimates are important; for example:
• Gardeners choose different plants for sunny, shady or windy parts of the garden
• Land near water is often cooler than land further inland
• Land close to trees will be less windy
• Places facing south in the UK are warmer than those facing north.

Earlier in this chapter (page 45)

Activities

Going on a temperature safari around your school:

1 Draw a plan of your school. Mark on
a two warm areas
b two cool areas
c two shady areas
d two windy areas.
Give reasons for your choices.

Rural and urban differences

There are also differences in climate between built-up (urban) areas and countryside (rural). In the cities, roads and buildings heat up more quickly during the day. Traffic in cities creates heat. Cities are at least 1°C warmer than rural areas during the day. At night the surfaces will slowly release heat. Cities remain 4°C warmer than the surrounding rural areas at night.

▽ **Figure 3.22** New York street scene

Activity

2 Study Figure 3.22. Suggest a reason why this street would be warm in the summer and windy in the winter.

Explaining patterns

A geographer can describe the climate of an area by asking these questions:

- How far is it from the Equator?
- How far is it from the sea?
- How high is the area above sea level?
- What is the **prevailing wind**?

As you read the information describing the climates of the UK and Algeria, try to remember these four questions.

Frontal rainfall

Frontal rain happens when warm air meets cold air. This forms a **front**. The warmer air condenses and forms cloud. The warm air rises and cools.

Relief rainfall

Relief rainfall is caused when warmer air is forced to rise over hills. As the warm air rises, it cools and condenses to form clouds. As the clouds pass over the hills, the water droplets fall as rain.

▽ **Figure 3.23** Rainfall diagrams

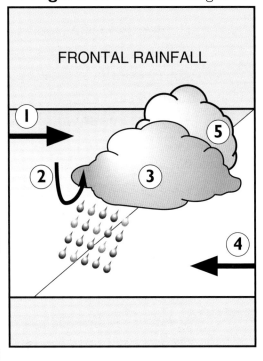

Activities

5 Copy out the diagrams in Figure 3.23 and then add the following labels to show how relief and frontal rainfall occur in Britain:

Frontal Rain
- water vapour condenses and turns into water droplets
- warmer air from the south
- clouds form
- colder air from the north
- warm air rises up over the cold air

Relief Rain
- warm air is forced to cool as the land gets higher
- moist air is forced upwards over the mountains
- air cools and condenses, turning into water droplets, clouds form

Comparing the UK with Algeria

Temperate maritime climate

The UK is located west of the **continent** of Europe. It is between 50 and 60 degrees north of the Equator. The UK has a **temperate climate**. This means temperatures are mild, never too warm or too cold.

We have rainfall throughout the year. Moist winds blow across the Atlantic Ocean and bring around 900 mm of rain each year.

The prevailing **winds** are from the west. These winds affect our climate. In summer, the winds blow over the cool Atlantic Ocean. These winds cool the summer temperatures. In winter, the winds blow over a warmer Atlantic Ocean. These help keep our winter temperatures mild. This is the **maritime** influence.

Hot desert climate

Algeria is located on the northern part of the Sahara desert. The Sahara desert is 10 to 30 degrees north of the Equator. The Sahara's location means that the climate is hot and dry.

The summer temperatures are very hot, up to 45°C during the day. The sun is directly overhead in the Sahara. Warm winds that blow across the Sahara keep the land dry. The sun is still high in the winter's sky. The temperatures are warm. Night times are cold in the desert. There is no cloud cover to trap the heat from the land.

Africa is a large continent. As winds blow across this dry, hot continent, they lose moisture. The winds are dry. There is very little rainfall. Some areas get less than 200 mm per year. Some areas only have rainfall for part of the year. When it does rain, the sun-baked soil cannot soak up the water. Instead it floods over the land. These are called **flash floods**.

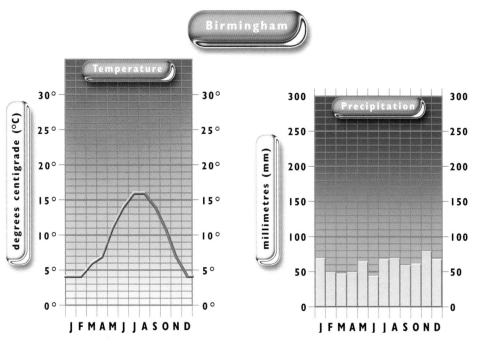

△ **Figure 3.24** Climate graph for Birmingham (altitude 163m)

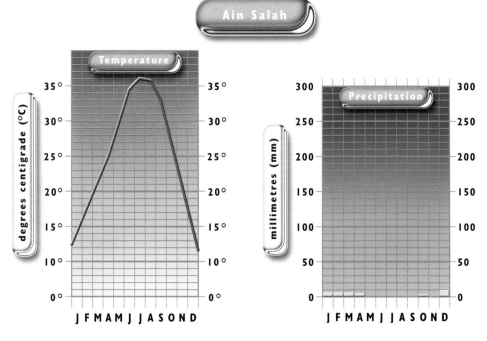

△ **Figure 3.25** Climate graph for Sahara Desert, Ain Salah, Algeria (altitude 293m)

1 Using information in the text and climate graphs, copy and complete the table below (Figure 3.26).

Feature	Birmingham	Ain Salah
Latitude		
Altitude		
Warmest month		
Coolest month		
Annual temperature range		
Wettest month		
Driest month		
Estimated annual rainfall		

△ **Figure 3.26**

2 Use the figures in your table to compare the climates of Birmingham and Ain Salah. Describe the similarities and differences. Useful phrases to include are:

SIMILAR TO	LESS THAN
BUT	HIGHER / LOWER
BOTH	HOTTER / COLDER
MORE THAN	DRIER / WETTER

Assessment task

Background

You have been asked to help design an information leaflet or display for the Eden Centre in Cornwall.

Task

Design Brief

Your job is to provide information about the plants that live in the hot deserts. You are to design an information leaflet or display. This should explain how plants manage to live in a hot desert area.

Useful sources of information are:
• Geography textbooks
• Library books (and Encarta)
• Internet sites such as www.desertusa.com
• Search engines such as Google (www.google.com) or Ask Jeeves (www.askjeeves.com).

Try to answer these questions in your work:
• What is a desert climate like?
• What does a desert look like?
• What kinds of plants live in a desert?
• What is special about these plants, e.g. their leaves, roots, how they store water?
• Suggest what the ideal desert plant should look like.

Use diagrams and text to present your information. Remember to make it lively and interesting for the visitors.

In the Atacama desert, Chile, no rain was recorded in the 400 years before 1971.

The longest drought in the UK was in 1893, when London did not receive any rain for 73 days.

The coldest place where people live is Norilsk, in Russia. The average temperature for the year is –10.9°C. The coldest recorded temperature ever was –89.2°C in Antarctica in 1983.

The highest amount of rainfall in 24 hours was 1 870 mm in La Reunion Island, Indian Ocean in 1952.

The wettest place is Mawsynran, in India, with 11 873 mm per year on average.

The highest amount of rainfall within one minute was 31.2 mm, recorded in the USA in 1956.

The fastest wind speed recorded on Earth is 231 mph (371 kmph), in New Hampshire, USA, in 1934.

The fastest wind speed recorded in the UK is 144 mph (231 kmph) in Scotland in 1967.

The hottest place where people live is Djibouti, where the average temperature is 30°C.

The hottest recorded temperature ever was 57.7°C at Al' Aziziyah in Libya in 1922.

The highest temperature ever recorded in the UK was 37.1°C.

Activities

1 Which of these records do you think is the most amazing? Why?

2 Look back through all of the work you have done for this unit. Write down the three most interesting things you have learnt.

△ **Figure 3.27** Weather facts

How does hair provide a living?

Before ...

△ **Figure 4.1**

Rasu and his family are pilgrims. They have travelled to the temple at Sri Venkatasvara to offer their hair to the Hindu god Vishnu. Barbers who work near the temple shave a strip of hair from each pilgrim to claim their scalp. The temple is paid for the hair it sells on. In some cases the people who give their hair are paid.

△ **Figure 4.2**

Hair from barber shops, temples and from villages is bought. The best quality hair is used to make wigs. The rest is sold to chemical companies for use in food and medicine manufacture.

Activities

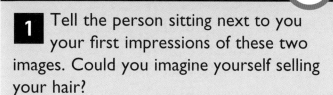

1 Tell the person sitting next to you your first impressions of these two images. Could you imagine yourself selling your hair?

2 What questions would you like to ask the people who sell their hair to find out more about their lives?

The World of Work

There are different jobs in many types of industry. These can be put into different categories.

- **Primary industry** produces raw materials from the land or sea.
- **Secondary industry** turns the raw materials into a finished product.
- **Tertiary industry** provides help and advice.
- **Quaternary industry** is information technology.

You can decide in which category a job is by asking three questions.

First, are they taking anything from the natural world?
- Yes means a primary job.
- No means asking a second question.

Are they making something?
- Yes means a secondary job.
- No means a tertiary or quaternary occupation.

Lastly, are they helping people?
- Yes would suggest a tertiary job.
- No may mean quaternary.

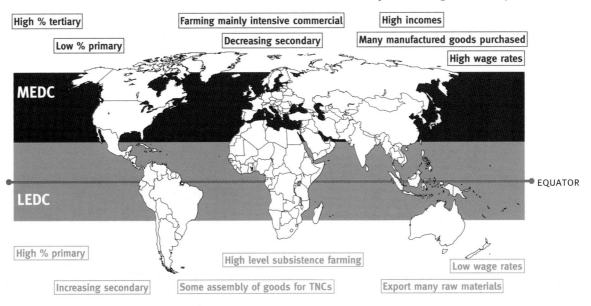

△ **Figure 4.3** Comparing countries

Comparing countries

MEDCs have few primary workers. In MEDCs the largest employers are the tertiary and secondary sectors. These jobs pay higher wages. MEDCs collect taxes to pay for public **services** like health and education. People spend money on leisure activities and consumer goods. This creates more tertiary jobs.

LEDCs have a large primary sector, especially agriculture. LEDCs have few manufacturing jobs. People earn a living by creating jobs in the tertiary sector. These form an **informal economy** that meets many local needs. Government cannot collect taxes from these workers to improve public services.

What does it mean for me?

EACH DAY I WORK... I EARN...

I HAVE...

I LIVE IN...

MY NAME IS...

who?

what?

where?

why?

I LIVE IN...

EACH DAY I...

I HAVE...

△ **Figure 4.4** Child labourer

▷ **Figure 4.5** Children in Britain

Activities

1 **a** Write a list of five jobs you would expect a 12-year-old to do in the UK.

b Write a list of five jobs a 12-year-old would do in an LEDC.

c Are your lists the same?

d Suggest why they might be different.

2 Study Figures 4.4 and 4.5.

a Suggest three questions you could ask about how each will earn their living in the future.

b Suggest why there is likely to be a difference between the answers.

How and why is the United Kingdom employment structure changing?

Each area has different types of industry. The jobs in an area can tell us about its industrial history and geography.

REGION		PRIMARY%	SECONDARY%	TERTIARY%
1	South East	2	14	84
2	London	Less than 1	8	92
3	Eastern	2	18	80
4	South West	2	17	81
5	East Midlands	3	26	71
6	West Midlands	1	27	72
7	North West	1	21	78
8	Yorkshire/Humbershire	2	22	76
9	North	1	23	76
10	Wales	2	22	76
11	Scotland	3	16	81
12	Northern Ireland	4	18	78

△ **Figure 4.6** Regional employment structure, 1999

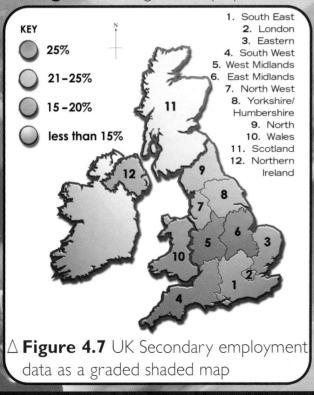

△ **Figure 4.7** UK Secondary employment data as a graded shaded map

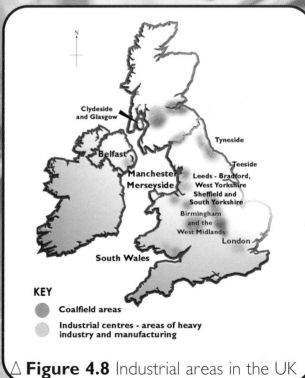

△ **Figure 4.8** Industrial areas in the UK

Some reasons for the changes

In recent years, many industrial areas have changed. There are a number of reasons for this:

- foreign competition

- raw materials running out, for example, no coal or iron ore left to mine

- new materials, for example, plastics replacing metal

- robot technology replacing workers, for example, in car manufacturing

- cheaper to make goods in LEDCs

- old factories are expensive to update.

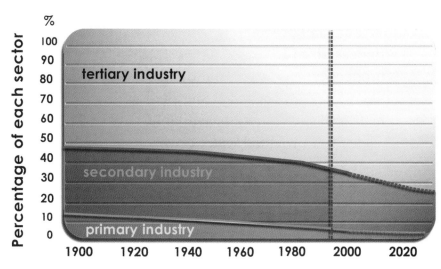

△ **Figure 4.9** Changes in the United Kingdom employment structure

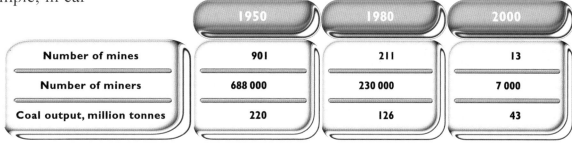

	1950	1980	2000
Number of mines	901	211	13
Number of miners	688 000	230 000	7 000
Coal output, million tonnes	220	126	43

△ **Figure 4.10** Changes in coal mining

Activities

1 Look at Figure 4.6.
   a Which are the top three regions for primary industry in the UK?
b Which are the top three regions for tertiary industry in the UK?
c On a regional map of the UK, plot these regions. Write a sentence to describe your map.

2 Look at Figure 4.10. Draw three bar charts to show the following:
   a how the number of mines have changed
a how the number of miners have changed
b how the amount of coal output has changed.

3 Suggest a reason why the coal industry has changed.

What has happened to Sheffield Steel?

World trends

World steel production has increased. In some countries steel production has fallen. Sheffield has a long steel history. Sheffield had local raw materials available. The rivers provided water power. There was a huge demand for steel. However, steel-making became expensive and the raw materials ran out. The area has few factories left.

The UK imports steel from LEDCs. In 1948, the top steel producers were the USA and UK. By 1995, the top steel producers were Japan and China. These countries have modern steelworks, plentiful raw materials and a cheap labour force (Figure 4.12).

	1948	1970	1980	1990	1995
World	155	593	690	723	720

△ **Figure 4.11** World steel production (million tonnes)

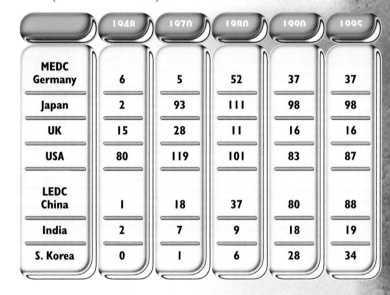

	1948	1970	1980	1990	1995
MEDC Germany	6	5	52	37	37
Japan	2	93	111	98	98
UK	15	28	11	16	16
USA	80	119	101	83	87
LEDC China	1	18	37	80	88
India	2	7	9	18	19
S. Korea	0	1	6	28	34

△ **Figure 4.12** Selected steel production

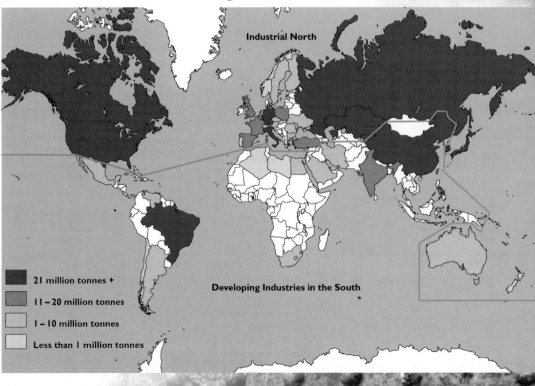

Industrial North

Developing Industries in the South

- 21 million tonnes +
- 11 – 20 million tonnes
- 1 – 10 million tonnes
- Less than 1 million tonnes

△ **Figure 4.13** World steel producers

Activities

1 World trend

Use Figure 4.11 to complete these sentences:

a The world production of steel has ....

b Steel production in 1948 was .... million tonnes.

c Steel production in 1995 was .... million tonnes.

2 Steel production in MEDCs
Study Figure 4.12.

a Draw a bar chart to show steel production for the UK.

b Is steel production increasing or decreasing?

c Are all MEDCs like the UK?

3 Steel production in LEDCs

a Draw a bar chart to show the steel production in South Korea.

b Is steel production increasing or decreasing?

c Are all LEDCs like South Korea?

4 Summary: Comparing LEDCs with MEDCs

Use the writing frame on the right to draft an account of world steel production. Use the words and phrases in the word box to help. You can use each word more than once.

Word box	
increased	
decreased	
fallen	
gone up	
15 million tonnes	
no steel	
34 million tonnes	
16 million tonnes	
increase	
decrease	

Introduction
This account will describe ....

In MEDCs
In MEDCs steel production has ....
In the UK steel production has ....
In 1948 the UK produced ....
In 1995 the UK produced ....

In LEDCs
In LEDCs steel production has ....
In South Korea steel production has ....
In 1948 South Korea produced ....
In 1995 South Korea produced ....

Conclusion
Since 1948 world steel production has ....
In the future, steel production in MEDCs will ....
A reason for this is ....
In the LEDCs steel production will continue to ....
A reason for this is ....

What happened to the Lower Don valley?

The Lower Don Valley was the centre of Sheffield Steel production. Only one large producer and a few specialist works remain. Since 1960 18 000 steel jobs have been lost. For every steel job, another three jobs are lost. Unemployment increased and the steelworks became derelict. There were no other industries in the area. The Lower Don Valley went into economic decline and became an industrial wasteland.

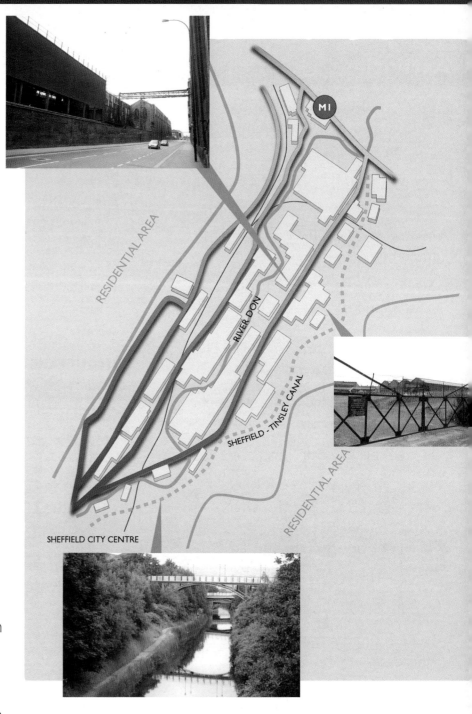

▷ **Figure 4.14** Sketch map locating the Lower Don Valley

〉 Regeneration

In 1990 the Sheffield Development Corporation (SDC) was set up. The aim was to redevelop the Lower Don Valley by:

- creating 18 000 new jobs
- building Meadowhall
- attracting new industries
- improving transport links
- clearing the **derelict** land.

Many local people feel they have not benefited. They lack the skills to be employed. New companies bring existing workers with them. Many new jobs are low paid, low skilled and part-time.

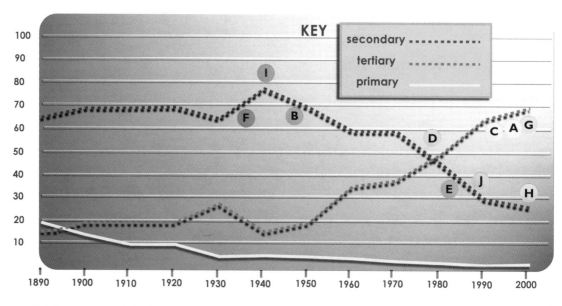

△ **Figure 4.15** Changes in the employment structure of Sheffield

Activities

1 Study the statements below carefully and decide which one you think matches best with the points marked by letters on Figure 4.15.

1 Jim gets a job as a security guard at Meadowhall.	2 Jim loses his job at the steelworks.	3 Marjorie takes her grandson to see 'Disney on Ice' at the Arena.	4 Paul gets a job at Abbey National's call centre in the Don Valley.	5 River Don is yellow with pollution.
6 World War Two means high demand for Sheffield steel.	7 China's steel production overtakes the UK.	8 Don Valley used as location for nuclear war films.	9 Many school leavers get jobs with steel firms.	10 Kingfishers seen living by River Don.

2 Study the photos in Figure 4.14.

a Suggest some adjectives to describe these photographs.

b Use these adjectives to write a sentence about each photograph.

Where does industry locate and why?

Industry locates where there is good **access** to its suppliers and market. Different industries have different needs.

Figure 4.16 shows these location factors. An important factor is what the area looks like.

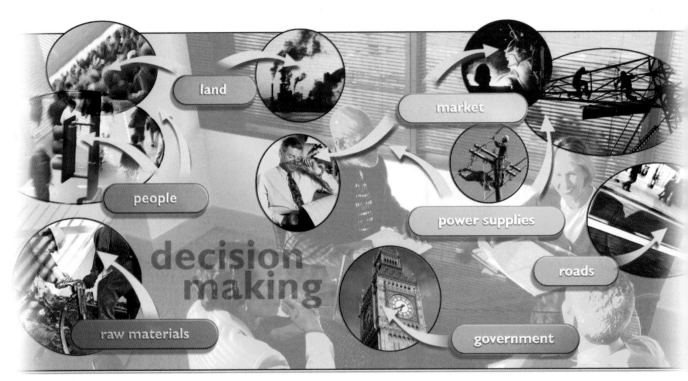

land

people

raw materials

decision making

market

power supplies

roads

government

△ **Figure 4.16** Location factors

Sometimes an industry will carry on despite losing the reason for its being there. Sheffield steel continues because of its tradition and skilled workforce. It now imports its raw materials. This is **industrial inertia**.

Industries must be able to meet their customers needs. A football club can be a large employer. What jobs does a football club provide?

Chesterfield Football Club built a ground at Saltergate in 1874. It is close to the town centre in a dense housing area. The Saltergate ground needs to be improved. The choice is to either redevelop Saltergate or move to a purpose-built ground.

Figure 4.18 shows some possible locations.

Where should Chesterfield FC be?

On match days Saltergate is **congested** and parking is difficult. The local residents complain of the disruption and noise.

The new site needs car parking space, access to public transport, and must be away from residential areas.

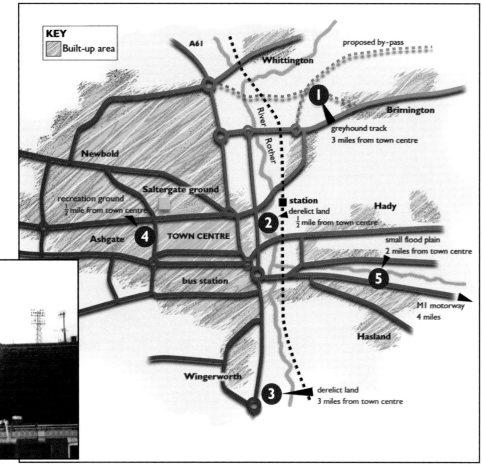

△ **Figure 4.17** Saltergate

△ **Figure 4.18** Some possible locations for Chesterfield FC

Activities

1 Describe the problems of Saltergate as shown in Figure 4.17.

2 Give one advantage and one disadvantage for each of the possible sites shown on Figure 4.18. Use the table (right) to help.

3 Which site would you choose for your new stadium?

4 Draw a plan of a new stadium for Chesterfield. Add labels to show how you meet the needs.

5 Design a poster to say why your choice is the best site.

Site	Advantage	Disadvantage
1 Greyhound track	Away from home	No public transport
2 Station		
3 Wingerworth		
4 Ashgate		
5 Hasland		

Who makes the clothes you wear?

£23 billion is spent on clothes in Britain each year. Over half of the clothes' production comes from overseas. Most come from Asia where the garment industry has grown rapidly. But many clothes factories in Britain have closed. 800 000 jobs have been lost.

In Asia, there are lower costs. Many companies have relocated in Asia. The price of making clothes has become cheaper. Sports and fashion shops have insisted on cheaply produced clothes from their suppliers.

◁ **Figure 4.19** A jeans factory in Ras Jebel, Tunisia. The trained machinists earn 58p an hour.

In Asia this work provides much needed income. Many have to work long hours, in poor conditions for very low wages (Figure 4.20). There is always pressure to reduce costs or lose the overseas clothes contracts.

In West Africa, cotton is grown. The chemicals used by farmers damages their health. Cotton pickers earn 50p a day. The farmers make £10 profit per ton of cotton. Growing cotton reduces the soil fertility and yields fall. Land is used for cotton rather than growing food crops

The brass zips or jean rivets made in Japan use zinc and copper ore from South Africa. Mining pollutes the local area and damages people's health. There are few other jobs.

Clothing is a global industry. There are worldwide links between producers and consumers. Clothes labels identify where a garment is made but not the workplace conditions. As we demand cheaper clothes and fashion, there is a pressure to keep wages low and working conditions poor.

Country	Population	Wages £ per hour in textiles	Annual income per person $
China	1 185 000 000	0.35	620
Bangladesh	118 342 000	0.38	240
Indonesia	198 644 000	0.30	980
USA	263 563 000	6.80	27 000
UK	58 306 000	6.50	18 700

△ **Figure 4.20** Comparing incomes in textile producing countries

△ **Figure 4.21** Replica football shirts

Activities

1 **a** Find the country of origin for five items of your clothing.

b As a class produce a summary table for each item of clothing and country.

c Present this information on a world outline as a dot map. Use one dot for each item of clothing.

d Which part of the world has the most dots?

e Suggest a reason why this area has the most dots.

2 **a** With a partner, brainstorm at least ten jobs in the making of a replica shirt (Figure 4.21). Write these on separate pieces of paper.

b Suggest how much you think each job would be paid.

c Arrange these jobs in order of wages from lowest to highest.

d Which jobs do you think would be found in an LEDC and in an MEDC?

e Suggest a reason for your list finalised in 2c.

What are transnational companies: are they good or bad?

Sportswear: a case study

Sportswear is big business. Companies spend a lot on advertising. This includes sponsorship of national football teams and famous sports people.

American and European companies have moved to Asia. Asia has a cheap and flexible workforce. Indonesia makes 7 million pairs of sports shoes a month. One company employs 90 000 workers. The minimum wage is $2.46 per day. Some companies think this is still too high. Firms are moving production to China and former European communist states, where wage costs are lower.

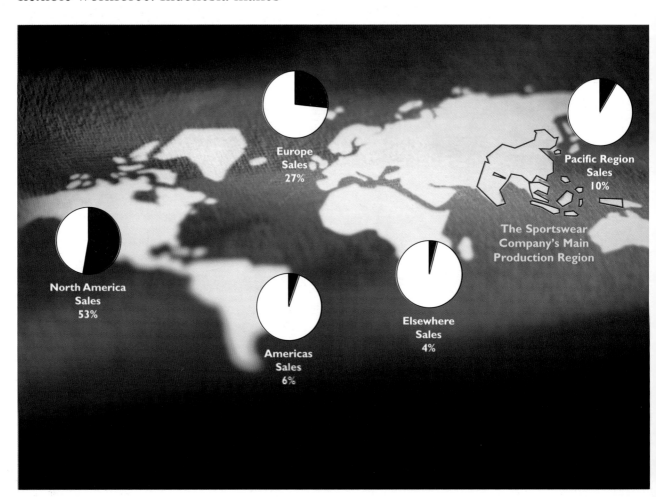

△ **Figure 4.22** A leading sportswear company's worldwide sales

Transnational companies (TNCs) operate on a worldwide scale. Figure 4.23 shows where a company gets the materials for a pair of £20 jeans.

Transnational companies often earn more money than the countries with which they trade. This makes TNCs very important in LEDCs. Why do LEDCs want TNCs to be in their countries? What are the benefits for the LEDC?

△ **Figure 4.23** Origin of the components for a major jeans company

▽ **Figure 4.24** Advantages and disadvantages of TNCs to LEDCs

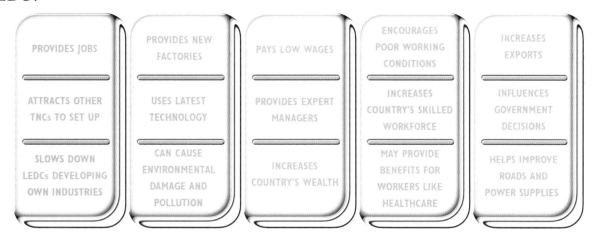

PROVIDES JOBS

ATTRACTS OTHER TNCs TO SET UP

SLOWS DOWN LEDCs DEVELOPING OWN INDUSTRIES

PROVIDES NEW FACTORIES

USES LATEST TECHNOLOGY

CAN CAUSE ENVIRONMENTAL DAMAGE AND POLLUTION

PAYS LOW WAGES

PROVIDES EXPERT MANAGERS

INCREASES COUNTRY'S WEALTH

ENCOURAGES POOR WORKING CONDITIONS

INCREASES COUNTRY'S SKILLED WORKFORCE

MAY PROVIDE BENEFITS FOR WORKERS LIKE HEALTHCARE

INCREASES EXPORTS

INFLUENCES GOVERNMENT DECISIONS

HELPS IMPROVE ROADS AND POWER SUPPLIES

Activities

1 Suggest a definition of a transnational company (TNC).

2 Use Figure 4.23 to describe why this TNC is a global company.

3 Give one advantage and one disadvantage of TNCs to LEDCs.

4 Imagine you are a clothes worker in Asia.

a Write and draw what your working conditions are like.

b Suggest three things that would improve the working conditions.

In the 1980s the steel industry collapsed. Industry in the Lower Don Valley, Sheffield, closed down. The area became derelict. Development projects have helped to regenerate the area. The largest has been the Meadowhall Shopping Centre. There are other possible development projects. These include:

A small airport
The runway will have to be one km long. It needs to be in an open area.

A technology park
This will need a small area to build small units.

A retail park
This will need a large flat area to build stores, space for car parking. Easy access to the motorway would be useful.

A group of workshops
This will need a small area to build factory units.

An athletics stadium
This will need main road access with public transport. It will need space for car parking. It will need a large area to build a sports stadium with the stands and other facilities.

An international arena
This will need main road access to the motorway. It could share parking space with the stadium. This will need good public transport.

▽ **Figure 4.25** An aerial view of the Lower Don Valley

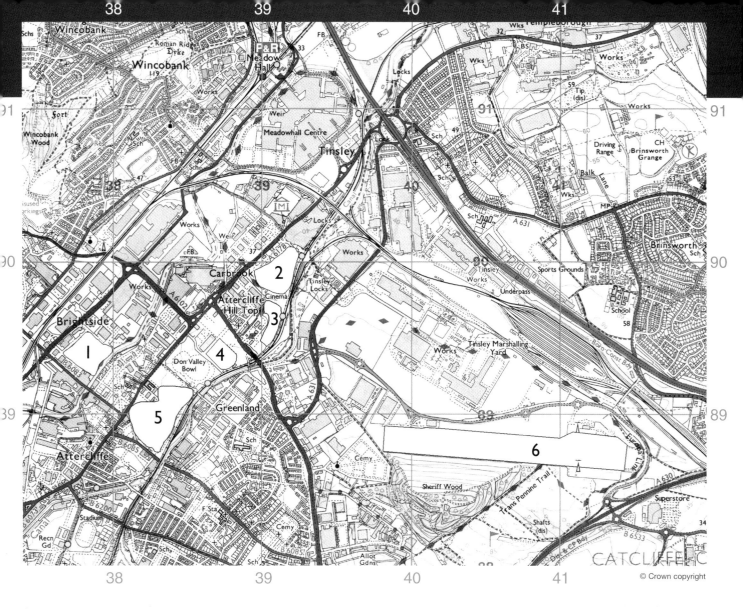

△ **Figure 4.26** OS map Lower Don Valley

© Crown copyright

Tasks

1 **a** Draw or trace an outline map of Figure 4.26. Mark on the following features:

- **in red:** the main roads
- **in dark blue:** the M1 motorway
- **in blue:** the canal and the River Don
- **in black:** the railway
- **in orange:** the Meadowhall Shopping Centre

Add a key to your map.

b Shade and label each possible site, 1–6.

3 Read the notes about each proposed development. Study your map. Decide which would be the best location for each development. Label these on your map.

4 Give at least one reason for each of your decisions. Use these sentence starts to help:

I have decided to put the ..... at site .....
The reason for my decision is .....
This development also needs ..... so that .....

5 Suggest one other development that would help the Lower Don Valley. Locate this on your map. Use the sentence starts to explain your suggestion.

△ **Figure 4.27**

△ **Figure 4.28**

△ **Figure 4.29**

Activities

1 Choose one of the photographs opposite.

a Suggest what economic activity is there.

b How might this activity change in the future?

c Suggest a reason why.

d Is this activity connected with any other jobs?

e Draw a labelled sketch of one of the photographs. Describe why this area might be attractive to a new business.

2 Read through all the work you have done about economic activities. Write a sentence to describe:

a One thing that has surprised you.

b One thing about industry in an LEDC.

c How industry is changing in the UK.

d Compile a class list on the board.

3 Make a list of the skills you have used. Which ones are you going to use again?

4 a What job or career would you like to have when you leave school?

b Where would you go to work?

c Compare your ideas with the rest of the class.

National Parks

What is special about a National Park?

A **National Park** is an area that has been given special planning laws to try and make sure that it is looked after. It is an area of natural beauty. People live and work in National Parks.

△ Figure 5.2

△ Figure 5.1

▽ Figure 5.3

streams
quiet
wild
traditional
countryside
pretty
peaceful
free
clean
crowded
open
villages
boring
isolated
cottages
tourists
moors
daytrips
old
green
footpaths
farmland
relaxed

△ **Figure 5.6** Responses to the photographs

△ **Figure 5.4**

▽ **Figure 5.5**

Activities

1 Read the words in Figure 5.6. Match these words with the photographs in Figures 5.1 to 5.5.

2 Which words did you use more than once?

3 Think of three adjectives of your own for each photograph that helps describe it.

4 Write three sentences to describe what you would expect to see on a visit to a National Park.

What do we already know about parks?

We all have a picture in our minds when we hear the word 'park'. Most people who live in towns think of a children's playground in a **public park**, like Figure 5.7.

▽ **Figure 5.7** A public park

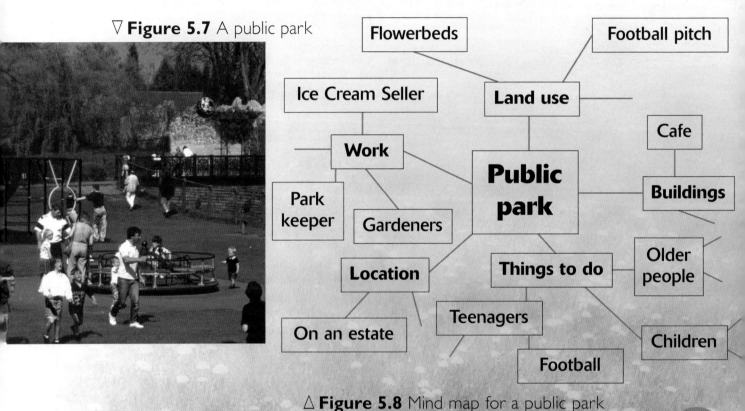

Flowerbeds

Ice Cream Seller

Work

Park keeper

Gardeners

Location

On an estate

Land use

Football pitch

Public park

Cafe

Buildings

Things to do

Older people

Teenagers

Football

Children

△ **Figure 5.8** Mind map for a public park

Activities

1 Name three examples of local parks in your area.

2 Work in a small group. Complete a copy of the mind map above to describe a local park you know well.

3 Use your ideas from page 85 to draw a mind map for a National Park.

4 List three ways that National Parks are the same as public parks. Now list three ways they are different.

How to draw a mind map

a Start with a topic that you want to investigate in the middle of your paper.

b Add on the main ideas that are part of the topic. These ideas are the main branches leading away from the middle.

c Add to your ideas, dividing the branch as you think of points you want to add.

d You do not have to finish one branch before you add things to another branch – just note down your ideas as they come to you.

e Use a big piece of paper and colours. Add pictures to make your ideas clear.

Activities

5 The statements listed below could be about three types of park – a public park (Figure 5.7), a National Park (Figures 5.1–5.6), and a third type of park, a **theme park** (Figure 5.9).

- Discuss what a theme park, a National Park and a public park are.
- Decide which statements are most likely to be true for a theme park, which for a National Park, and which for a public park.
- You can use individual statements for more than one park.
- Now write out your description of each park.

Which of the three types of park are the most likely to:

1 charge money to get in
2 provide a home for wildlife
3 have things for small children to do
4 provide a full family day out
5 be within walking distance of your house
6 have a burger bar
7 provide new activities each year
8 suffer from vandalism
9 attract people from a wide area
10 have people who live and work there
11 be owned by the local authority
12 cause annoyance to local residents
13 employ people to look after the park
14 be educational
15 offer opportunities for outdoor activities
16 be advertised on TV

Remember

There is no right answer to this activity. What is important are your reasons.

When you have finished your discussions, use the speaking frames below to feedback to the rest of the class.

'One statement we found easy to place was ... because ...'

'One statement we argued about was ... because ...'

'We found it difficult to place the statement about ... because ...'

◁ **Figure 5.9** A theme park

Where are the National Parks in England and Wales?

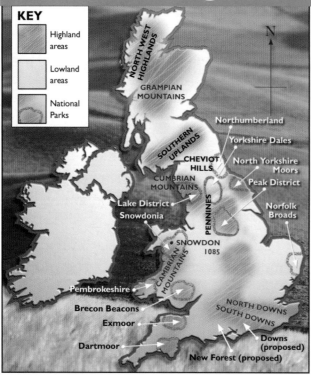

△ **Figure 5.10** Location of the National Parks and relief of England and Wales

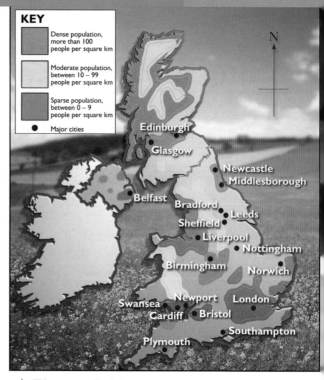

△ **Figure 5.11** Population distribution in England and Wales

In England and Wales National Parks were created in 1949. They were made to protect the countryside and look after it for future generations to enjoy. Each of the National Parks has its own managers who work with landowners. They try to do two things: attract visitors and protect the beauty of the place.

Activities

1 Use the maps to decide whether the statements below are True, False or whether there is not enough evidence to tell.
- Most of the parks are in highland areas.
- Norfolk Broads is a lowland area.
- Northumberland will be the least visited National Park.
- The Yorkshire Dales park is close to Bradford.
- There are no big cities in National Parks.
- Brecon Beacons park is close to the big cities in Wales.

2 Discuss the statements below with your class. Choose one and complete it in your book.

'It's a good thing National Parks are far away from cities because …'

'It would be better if National Parks were close to cities because …'

What is the Peak District National Park like?

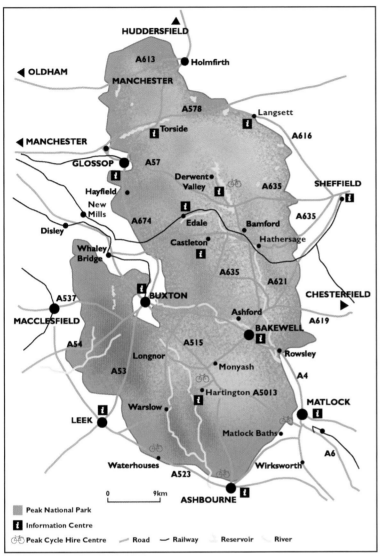

Peak National Park
Information Centre
Peak Cycle Hire Centre — Road — Railway — Reservoir — River

◁ **Figure 5.12**
Peak District

Castleton is a main **honeypot site** in the Peak District. This means it attracts many visitors who come to:

- visit the caverns in the limestone
- shop in the many tourist shops in the village
- eat in the tea rooms and cafes
- visit Peveril Castle
- walk along the many footpaths
- look around the pretty village.

Width ...?
Length ...?
Area of the park
Population 38 100
Nearby cities ...?

Number of visitors
22 million/year
Average amount spent
£6/person/day
Names of villages ...?

Honeypot sites
Castleton, Bakewell

Activities available ...?

Land owners
National Trust 5%
Forestry Commission 1%
Water Companies 14%
National Park 2%
Private 78%

Activities

△ **Figure 5.13** Castleton

3 Draw a poster to attract visitors to the Peak District, showing some of the activities available. Use the text and photos to get ideas.

How do people make a living in the Peak District?

△ **Figure 5.14** An OS extract showing the Castleton Area from OS Outdoor Leisure 1:25 000

© Crown copyright

The map (Figure 5.14) shows a small part of the Peak District National Park. This part is in Derbyshire. 22 million people visit the Peak District every year, some for day trips and some to stay for a holiday. But there are thousands of people who live and work in the Peak District all year. There are rules about the type of things that can be developed in a National Park. This might mean that fewer jobs are available for local people.

Activities

1 **a** Find places on the map where people might work.
Ask your teacher whether you should use four-or six-figure grid references to record them.
Here are three to help you get started.

Farm work at 143835, College at 167834 and ... at 152831.

b Make a list of all the jobs that might be done at each place.

2 Draw a bar graph to show these statistics of jobs in the Peak District:

services	11 000 people
manufacturing	3 500 people
farming	2 000 people
quarrying	1 400 people

3 Put the jobs you found in activity 1 into the groups you used on your graph in activity 2.
Which group have you found most jobs for?

4 Which of the jobs would have been affected by the 2001 foot and mouth outbreak?

> **Practise your map skills**

5 Which direction is it:
• from Castleton to Hope
• from Castleton to Hollins Cross
• from Castleton to Smalldale
• from Hope to the quarry?

6 The photo (Figure 5.13) was taken in this area. Which square do you think it was probably taken in?

7 How far is it in a straight line from:
• Hope to Castleton
• Treak Cliff Cavern to Peak Cavern
• Blue John Cavern to Hollins Cross?

8 Which grid square contains the higher point: 1382 or 1384?

9 What happens to the contours if you walk west from Castleton village towards Speedwell Cavern? What would it feel like to walk this route?

10 Draw a simple sketch map of Figure 5.14. Plot on main roads, settlements and tourist attractions. Describe the tourist attractions on your map.

How would you spend a day in the Peak District?

A family of two adults, a son aged 10 and a daughter aged 12, are going on a day trip to the Castleton area. They have £25 to spend. They like outdoor activities.

Activities

Use the map from page 90 and Figure 5.15 to plan a good day out for them.

Remember

Think about ways they could keep the cost down. Not all activities in National Parks cost money!

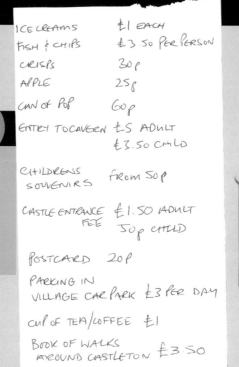

ICE CREAMS   £1 EACH
FISH & CHIPS   £3.50 PER PERSON
CRISPS   30p
APPLE   25p
CAN OF POP   60p
ENTRY TO CAVERN   £5 ADULT
                  £3.50 CHILD

CHILDRENS   FROM 50p
SOUVENIRS

CASTLE ENTRANCE   £1.50 ADULT
        FEE   50p CHILD

POSTCARD   20p

PARKING IN
VILLAGE CAR PARK £3 PER DAY

CUP OF TEA/COFFEE £1

BOOK OF WALKS
AROUND CASTLETON £3.50

△ **Figure 5.15** Price list

Fill in a copy of this table with your ideas

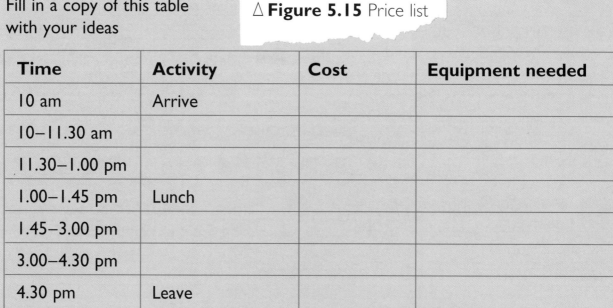

Time	Activity	Cost	Equipment needed
10 am	Arrive		
10–11.30 am			
11.30–1.00 pm			
1.00–1.45 pm	Lunch		
1.45–3.00 pm			
3.00–4.30 pm			
4.30 pm	Leave		

You could even offer alternative suggestions depending on the weather!
Now write a diary entry as if you had been on this day out.

What services are available in a National Park Village?

Services available for the residents of Castleton	
Grocer	3 general stores selling range of foods
Butcher	Nearest shop is in Hope
Baker	Nearest shop is in Hathersage
Greengrocer	Mobile shop visits once per week
Medical centre and chemist	Chemist in Hathersage. Medical centre in Hope
Post Office	In the village
School	Primary school in village, secondary in Hope
Police	Police house in the village, station at Hathersage
Church	C of E and Methodist churches in the village
Library	Mobile library visits once per week
Petrol	Available in the village
Services for visitors to Castleton	
B&B/Guest House	7
Hotels	4
Camping/caravan sites	4 (includes camping barn)
Youth hostels	1
Tourist shops/souvenirs	Numerous
Cafes	6
Information centre	1

There are also 6 pubs and a fish and chip shop which benefit both local residents and visitors.

△ **Figure 5.16** Services in Castleton
Source: www.peakdistrict.org

Activities

1 Make a list of the things people would buy most days.

2 How many of the things on your list could you buy in Castleton?

3 Where would you have to go to buy the other things?

4 Suggest why you cannot buy these things in Castleton.

5 With a partner make a list of the problems these people might have living in Castleton:

- a teenager
- a retired person with no car.

6 Which extra service do you think Castleton most needs? Suggest a reason for your answer.

7 List the services that you have locally. Where do you go shopping for food and other goods? How different is life where you live to life in Castleton?

What are National Parks like elsewhere?

KEY

NHS	National Historic Site
NHP	National Historic Park
NM	National Monument
NP	National Park
NPRES	National Preserve
NRA	National Recreation Ar
NS	National Seashore

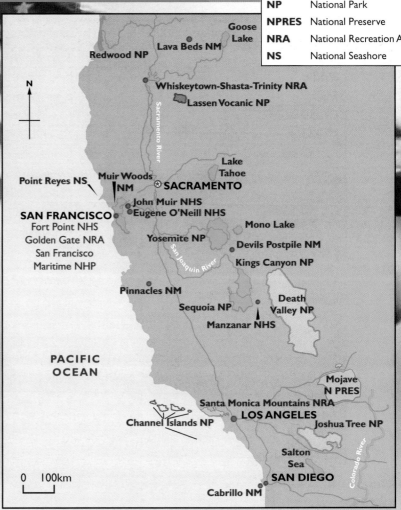

△ **Figure 5.17** National Parks and sites in California

The first National Parks were in the USA. People thought that the Indian heritage and the unspoilt landscape were in danger of disappearing. In 1872 Yellowstone in Wyoming became the world's first National Park.

The USA National Parks Service was set up to look after the increasing number of National Parks and other important sites. By 1999 there were 379 sites. This included places as different as the arctic wildernesses of Alaska, volcanoes in Hawaii and the Statue of Liberty in New York.

Activities

1 Study Figure 5.17. Use the key to list all the sites on the map under the correct heading.

2 What places can you think of in Britain that could be:

a a National Historic Site?

b a National Monument?

What is Yosemite National Park like?

Activities

This page has information about Yosemite National Park.

1 Use the information to design a tourist leaflet about Yosemite. Go to the following website for some additional information: www.nps.gov.yose

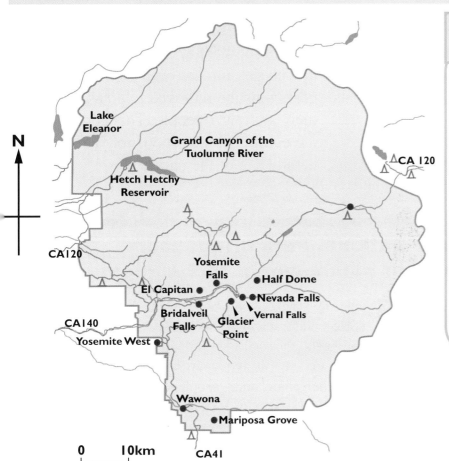

△ **Figure 5.18** Yosemite National Park

〉 Facilities for tourists

- Visitor Centre
- Yosemite Museum
- You can stay in tent cabins, luxury hotels or wilderness camps.
- You can ride bikes, birdwatch, climb, swim, horse-ride and canoe.

- You can learn about the area through educational programmes, stargazing and wildlife-viewing.

▷ **Figure 5.19** Photo of Mirror Lake, Yosemite Valley

What conflicts exist in Yosemite?

For thousands of years grizzly bears, black bears and mountain lions lived in Yosemite National Park, along with Native American people. In the 1840s tourists started to arrive. Now over 4 million people a year visit the park. The grizzly bears have all gone, and so have the Native Americans. One valley has been flooded to make a **reservoir** for San Francisco.

If you go down to the woods today ...

Most visitors go to the village in Yosemite Valley. Black bears are attracted there by the food that the tourists bring and the rubbish they leave. The bears use their great strength and intelligence to get hold of it. They will trash a car for a carrier bag that might contain food! They have even worked out how to get into the bear-proof bins. These bears must be removed to areas where there are fewer people. This is just one of the **conflicts** between visitors and the natural life of the parks.

Spring in Yosemite National Park brings more visitors and new bear management techniques

▷ **Figure 5.20** Car-breaking bear

As spring arrives, the Yosemite Park's black bears wake up from hibernation. The park staff are ready with some new ideas to stop the bears causing trouble. This year the staff will try scaring the bears with noisemakers. They will use rubber bullets to chase the bears out of the campsites. The staff hope that by making a noise and scaring the bears they will learn to stay away from the visitors and their food.

Bears who break into cars will be traced using hair they leave. The biologist will use DNA to identify the bears who damage cars for food.

Bear management schemes began in 1998. They have reduced the damage caused by bears. The cost of bear damage has fallen from approximately $650 000 to $125 000. No new adult bears live in the visitor areas. None have become used to people or human food.

To keep bears away from people, everyone has to help. Visitors must clean up after their visits. They must use the rubbish bins and use the storage lockers to keep their food. They must not keep food in their cars. If a bear is seen it should be reported on the Save-A-Bear hotline.

If people act responsibly, they will save the lives of the Yosemite bears. Yosemite National Park needs the public's help to care for the bears.

△ **Figure 5.21** Extract adapted from www.nps.gov.yose

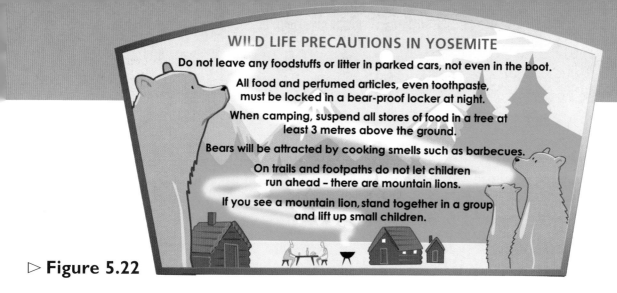

WILD LIFE PRECAUTIONS IN YOSEMITE

Do not leave any foodstuffs or litter in parked cars, not even in the boot.

All food and perfumed articles, even toothpaste, must be locked in a bear-proof locker at night.

When camping, suspend all stores of food in a tree at least 3 metres above the ground.

Bears will be attracted by cooking smells such as barbecues.

On trails and footpaths do not let children run ahead – there are mountain lions.

If you see a mountain lion, stand together in a group and lift up small children.

▷ **Figure 5.22**

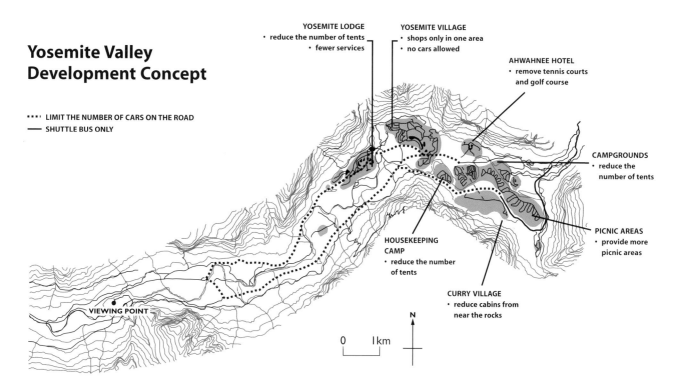

Yosemite Valley Development Concept

YOSEMITE LODGE
• reduce the number of tents
• fewer services

YOSEMITE VILLAGE
• shops only in one area
• no cars allowed

AHWAHNEE HOTEL
• remove tennis courts and golf course

CAMPGROUNDS
• reduce the number of tents

PICNIC AREAS
• provide more picnic areas

HOUSEKEEPING CAMP
• reduce the number of tents

CURRY VILLAGE
• reduce cabins from near the rocks

VIEWING POINT

▪▪▪▪ LIMIT THE NUMBER OF CARS ON THE ROAD
── SHUTTLE BUS ONLY

0   1 km

N

△ **Figure 5.23**

Activities

1 Read Figure 5.21 with your teacher. What danger does it describe? Choose a sentence that is an example of this danger.

2 Choose two changes on the map (Figure 5.23). Why do you think these changes were made?

3 Check on the Yosemite website www.nps.gov.yose – to find out the most recent number of bear incidents.

4 Design a poster to warn visitors to the park to take the wildlife precautions seriously.

What are World Heritage sites?

World Heritage sites are places that people have agreed are very important to save for the future. There are many different types of site. In 2001 there were 690 sites around the world. Once they are on the list no one can change them in any way; they should look the same for many years to come.

How does a place become a World Heritage site?

The World Heritage Committee has to consider the site. Is it a unique geological formation? Is it an important historical site? Is the site in need of protection and preservation?

Country	Site	Country	Site
Ecuador	Galapagos Islands	Italy	Venice and lagoon
Egypt	Pyramids, Giza	Italy	Pompeii
Kenya	Mt Kenya NP	USA	Yosemite NP
Ghana	Forts and castles, Accra	USA	Statue of Liberty, New York
South Africa	Robben Island	USA	Hawaii volcanoes
Tanzania	Zanzibar, stone town	Brazil	Brasilia
Austria	Town centre, Salzburg	Cuba	Old Havana
Canada	Rocky Mountain parks	Australia	Great Barrier Reef
France	Loire Valley	China	Great Wall
Germany	Cologne Cathedral	India	Taj Mahal
Greece	Acropolis, Athens	Japan	Hiroshima peace memorial
UK	Ironbridge Gorge	Nepal	Mount Everest
UK	Stonehenge	Jordan	Petra

△ **Figure 5.24** A selection of World Heritage sites

Activities

1 **a** Divide the sites in Figure 5.24 into NATURAL SITES and BUILDINGS. Look up any you don't know in the library.

b Now try to think of headings that will split each group into smaller groups.

2 Mark 10 of the sites onto a world map which has country outlines. Use an atlas to find out the names of the countries. Design a key to show the different types of site.

ICT activity

Visit the website of the World Heritage sites and complete the following tasks:

www.unesco.org/whc/ nwhc/pages/sites/main .htm

a Check the current number of World Heritage sites against the 690 when this book was written.

b How many sites are in the UK?

c Have you visited any of the UK sites?

d Write a postcard home as if you had really visited the site.

Future World Heritage sites?

△ **Figure 5.25** Castleton and the caverns, Peak District, UK

△ **Figure 5.26** Northumberland Coast, UK

Activities

3 Look at these photos. Which of your groups would these places fit into?

4 Could you suggest a place that you'd like to see as a heritage site? Suggest why.

◁ **Figure 5.27** Golden Gate Bridge, San Francisco, USA

Assessment tasks

Background

National Parks have always tried to encourage people to visit the countryside and also look after the environment. This leads to conflict. Too many visitors can damage rare plants. Too much farming or industry can destroy the landscape.

The land in a National Park is not owned by the government; there are many different owners.

National Park managers have a difficult job balancing everyone's needs.

Farmers
They want to make a living. They need to be sure that any visitors will not damage their land or harm the animals. They also have to pay to look after footpaths on their land. Some farmers make money with things like bed and breakfast.

Hang-gliding enthusiasts
They need to get to the hill tops by car so they can get their heavy equipment ready for launch.

Local residents
They know that many jobs depend on tourists. They dislike the fact that some visitors block drives with cars. They also get fed up with people looking into their homes. Living in a National Park means there can be problems if they want to extend their homes. They would like more services to be available.

Ramblers
They want to be able to walk over all areas. They feel paths should only be for walkers. They think farmers who block paths should be prosecuted.

Mountain bikers
They want to be able to cycle through the National Parks as the best hills are there. They would like special paths so they don't have to slow down for walkers. They don't like stiles and gates which slow them down.

Cement works
They need to dig limestone to make cement. They need a factory close to the quarry to cut down on transport costs. Then the cement needs to be moved to the big cities where it will be sold and used. Wider roads would be helpful for all the lorries.

△ **Figure 5.28** Who has an interest in the National Parks?

Tasks

1 Read Figure 5.28. The grid below (Figure 5.29) will help you to work out if there is a conflict between the various groups. The row for farmers has been done for you. Copy and complete the grid for the other seven groups. Work through each group one by one.

	Farmers	Mountain bikers	Hang gliders	Ramblers	Cement works	Local residents
Farmers		some problems	some problems		serious problems	
Mountain bikers						
Hang gliders						
Ramblers						
Cement works						
Local residents						

△ **Figure 5.29** Conflict matrix

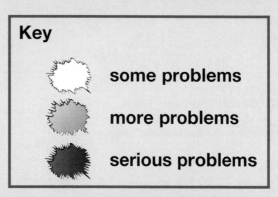

Key

⚪ some problems

🔘 more problems

⚫ serious problems

Tasks

2 Which three groups seem to cause most problems? Can you suggest a reason for this?

3 Copy and complete these sentences or show your ideas on a copy of Figure 5.30.

Mountain bikers might conflict with ramblers because …

Local residents will be most annoyed about … because …

The group that causes most conflict is … because …

4 Choose one group. Write five rules you think they should agree to when using the National Park.

5 Suggest three ideas to reduce conflict in the National Parks. Use the sentence starts to help you.

We need to try and reduce conflict in National Parks because …

My first idea is that …

This will mean … Also …

I think we could also try to … so that …

My final idea is … People would then be able …

Overall, I think …

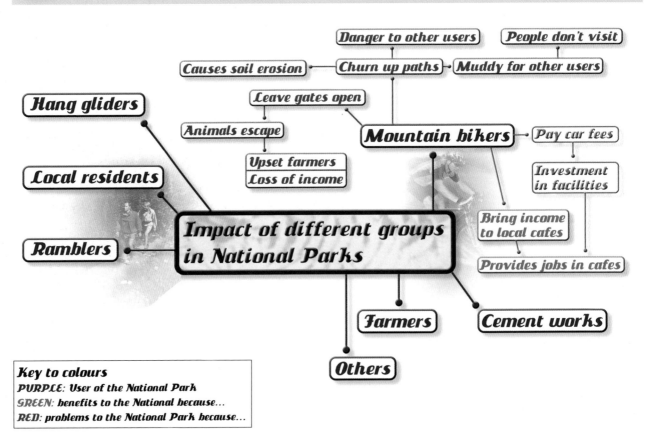

Danger to other users | **People don't visit**

Causes soil erosion ← **Churn up paths** → **Muddy for other users**

Hang gliders

Leave gates open

Animals escape

Mountain bikers → **Pay car fees**

Local residents

Upset farmers Loss of income

Investment in facilities

Impact of different groups in National Parks

Bring income to local cafes

Ramblers

Provides jobs in cafes

Farmers

Cement works

Others

Key to colours
PURPLE: User of the National Park
GREEN: benefits to the National because…
RED: problems to the National Park because…

△ **Figure 5.30** Mind map framework

Review

What have I learnt about National Parks?

Figure 5.31 is a list of words that should be familiar to you after completing the work on National Parks.

This exercise will check your understanding of the ideas and terms used.

1	Yosemite	*12*	horse riders
2	conflict	*13*	relief
3	Peak District	*14*	World Heritage site
4	historic site	*15*	rare plants
5	camping	*16*	farmer
6	rambling	*17*	cafe
7	resident	*18*	theme park
8	conservationist	*19*	Exmoor
9	park ranger	*20*	Norfolk Broads
10	fox	*21*	mountain lions
11	bear		

△ **Figure 5.31** National Park words

Activities

1 Start with Group A (Figure 5.32). Write out the words from Figure 5.31 that make up this group. Decide with a partner which word is the odd one out and why. Give a clear reason for your choice.

2 Work through the other groups, keeping a note of the choice of odd-one-out words and the reasons.

Group A	3	19	20	
Group B	10	11	21	
Group C	9	17	15	
Group D	8	10	16	
Group E	2	6	16	20
Group F	7	8	10	16
Group G	1	10	11	21
Group H	7	11	17	22
Group I	1	3	13	20
Group J	1	4	14	18

△ **Figure 5.32** Word groups

Is there a perfect place to live?

6 Few other people live here. I am a cattle farmer. I need plenty of grazing land. My family has always lived here. I think that too many people will spoil the world. City people need the countryside to get their food. 9

▷ **Figure 6.1**

6 My life is a very busy one. There are lots of people and always lots of things to do. I enjoy living in a busy place. I get fed up of the traffic jams and crammed trains. 9

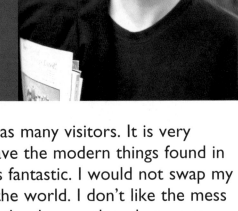

6 I live somewhere that has many visitors. It is very beautiful. We do not have the modern things found in the city. Our weather is fantastic. I would not swap my home for anywhere in the world. I don't like the mess visitors leave behind or the damage they do to our beautiful environment. 9

6 The place we live always has plenty to do. Our home is comfortable and has electricity. Why would we need to move? We're lucky. In the world, many poorer families cannot give their children a good life. 9

a

b

c

◁ **Figure 6.2**

d

e

f

Activities

1 Can you work out where the people in Figure 6.1 live? Choose from the places in Figure 6.2.

2 Suggest a reason why you have chosen the picture for each of the people.

3 **a** Where do you live?
b Describe what it is like.
c Do you like living here?
d Where else would you like to live?

What do you already know about population?

People live in many different places. Some can choose where to live, but others cannot. Humans need certain basic things to survive. They need a warm climate, water supply, food and shelter.

▷ **Figure 6.3** What affects your life?

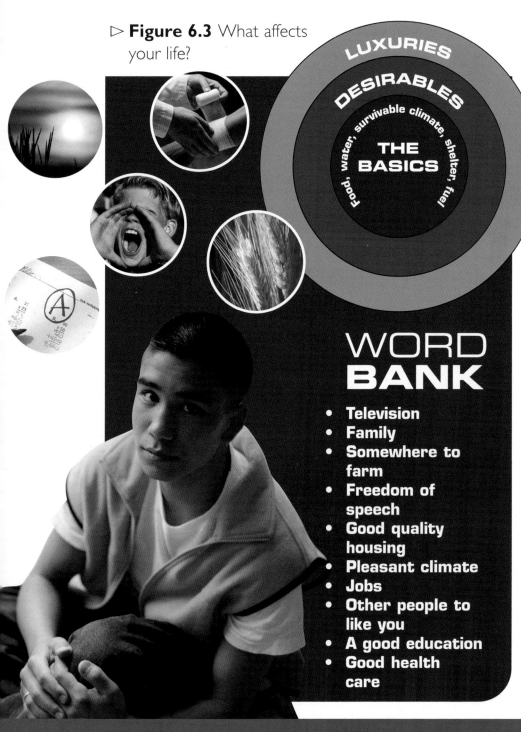

LUXURIES

DESIRABLES

Food, water, survivable climate, shelter, fuel

THE BASICS

WORD BANK

- Television
- Family
- Somewhere to farm
- Freedom of speech
- Good quality housing
- Pleasant climate
- Jobs
- Other people to like you
- A good education
- Good health care

Activities

1 Copy out the three-ringed circle in Figure 6.3. Add the labels 'The basics', 'Desirables' and 'Luxuries'.

2 Decide where to write in the words from the word bank.

3 Add at least three ideas of your own.

4 Look at the people on page 104. Choose one group of people. Draw a second chart. Write the ideas and words these people would use for this chart.

5 Compare your charts. How similar are they?

What's the big picture?

The next few pages have some connection with the theme of population. Figure 6.4 shows these ideas. This is an important page to look back at when you review your work.

▽ **Figure 6.4** Population concept map

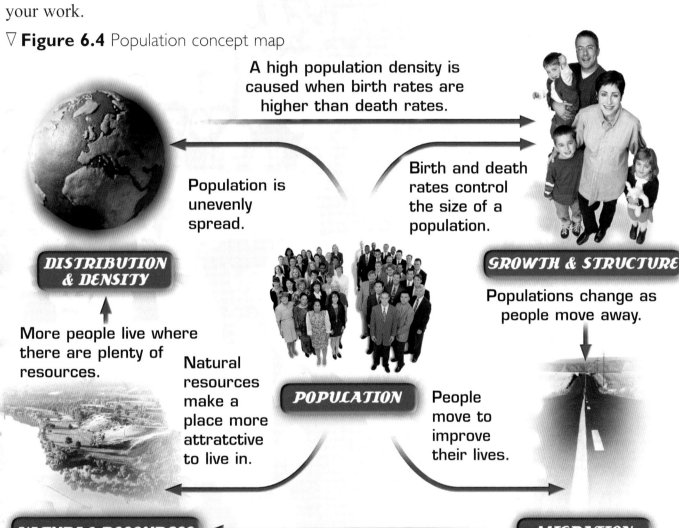

A high population density is caused when birth rates are higher than death rates.

Population is unevenly spread.

Birth and death rates control the size of a population.

DISTRIBUTION & DENSITY

GROWTH & STRUCTURE

Populations change as people move away.

More people live where there are plenty of resources.

Natural resources make a place more attratctive to live in.

POPULATION

People move to improve their lives.

NATURAL RESOURCES

People move for natural resources.

MIGRATION

What's so important about population?

Some people call population a problem because:
- there are too many people being born or dying
- there are crowded cities but empty countryside
- poor people want to move to richer parts of the world.

You need to know about population to understand:
- populations are changing
- population growth affects the environment
- what could be done.

What is population distribution?

△ Mumbai

△ Peruvian Andes

△ **Figure 6.5** World map showing population distribution

Figure 6.5 shows where large numbers of people live. The dots show a **population distribution**. This is an uneven distribution.

There are two reasons for this: positive reasons and negative reasons. Each of the positive and negative reasons has a link with the natural environment or the environment created by people.

Areas with large numbers of people have positive reasons associated with them. Empty areas tend to be negative places for people. In the UK 90% of people live in towns or cities, but why?

Activities

1 Use an atlas and Figure 6.5.

a Name three regions with a large population.

b Name three regions with very few people.

2 Copy Figure 6.6. Which are the positive factors that help people who live there?

▽ **Figure 6.6** Positive and Negative Factors

➕ POSITIVE & NEGATIVE FACTORS
➖ But which are which?

- Cold climate
- Flat land
- A good water supply
- A place to work
- Wars and fighting
- Easy to move around
- No natural resources for building or fuel
- A Government that doesn't listen to the people
- Good soils for growing crops
- Clean air and amazing views

What is population density?

Population density is the number of people per square kilometre of land. Figures 6.7 and 6.8 show that population density varies from place to place.

Urban areas have a high population density. Rural areas have a lower population density.

▽ **Figure 6.7** Town versus Country

Population distribution of the United Kingdom

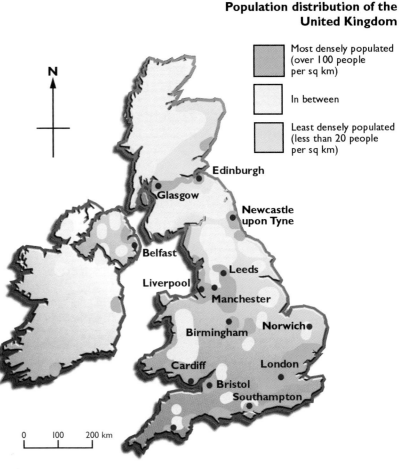

- Most densely populated (over 100 people per sq km)
- In between
- Least densely populated (less than 20 people per sq km)

N

0   100   200 km

△ **Figure 6.8** UK population distribution and density

Activities

3
  a On a piece of graph paper draw two 3 cm by 3 cm squares.

  b In one square shade in 10 of the smallest squares, space these out.

c In the second square, shade 100 small squares.

d One small square is one person. Which square has the highest population density?

e Write a sentence to describe population density.

4 Study Figure 6.8.

  a Where do most people live in the UK?

b Suggest why few people live in northern Scotland and central Wales.

5 What is the population density like in your area?

What is population growth?

The world's population is growing quickly. The total is updated every minute on this website: www.census.gov/main/www/popclock.html.

A population increases when there are more babies born than people dying. The **birth rate** is the number of babies that are being born each year. The **death rate** is the number of people who die each year. These are measured out of every 1 000 of a country's population. The difference between the birth and death rate is the **population growth rate**.

People moving into or out of a country also affect population. Population growth is greater in poorer countries than in richer countries. Poorer countries normally have a birth rate higher than the death rate.

What is it like to live in these countries with different birth and death rates?

ETHIOPIA

In Africa

Population: 58 million people

Area: 1.13 million km²

Life expectancy: 41 years

FRANCE

In Europe

Population: 58 million people

Area: 547 030 km²

Life expectancy: 78 years

ICT links

This website helps you create your own population pyramids:

www.census.gov/ipc/www/idbpyr.html

Births each year per 1 000 people

44.69   11.68

ETHIOPIA   **FRANCE**

▷ **Figure 6.9**
Birth rate: Ethiopia and France

Deaths each year per 1 000 people

21.25   9.12

ETHIOPIA   **FRANCE**

◁ **Figure 6.10**
Death rate Ethiopia and France

What is population structure?

A **population pyramid** shows by age how many men, women and children there are in a country. Population pyramids are used to study a country's population.

The population pyramids for Ethiopia and France are different shapes (Figure 6.11). Ethiopia has a wide base and a narrow top. France has a smaller base, bulges in the middle and then narrows at the top.

What is the point of studying population pyramids?

A wide base shows a high birth rate. A narrow top shows a high death rate. Studying a country's population pyramid can predict what the future population will be like and help plan for its needs.

Changes in the birth and death rates will affect how a country uses its resources. Fast growing populations will make it difficult to provide everybody with water, food, shelter, schools, hospitals and jobs.

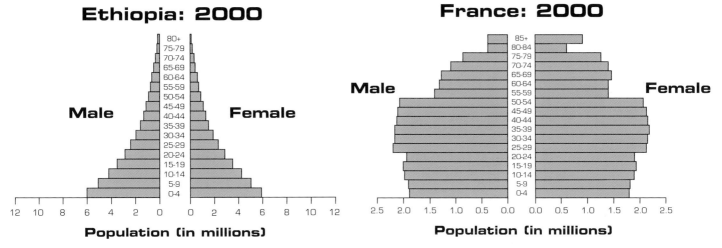

△ **Figure 6.11** Population pyramids: Ethiopia and France

Activities

1 Which of the two countries seen on this page has:

a the highest proportion of young people?

b the largest number of old people?

2 How do you think Ethiopia's population pyramid will change if:

a more people live longer?

b there is a lower birth rate?

What is population change?

The population change is the result of changes in the birth and death rate. There are a number of reasons for these changes. Geographers use a model, called the **population cycle**, to show how birth and death rates change over time. The population cycle has four stages (Figure 6.12).

Why do these changes take place?

Death rates fall as countries improve diet, living conditions and the way they fight disease. Britain has passed through most of the population cycle stages.

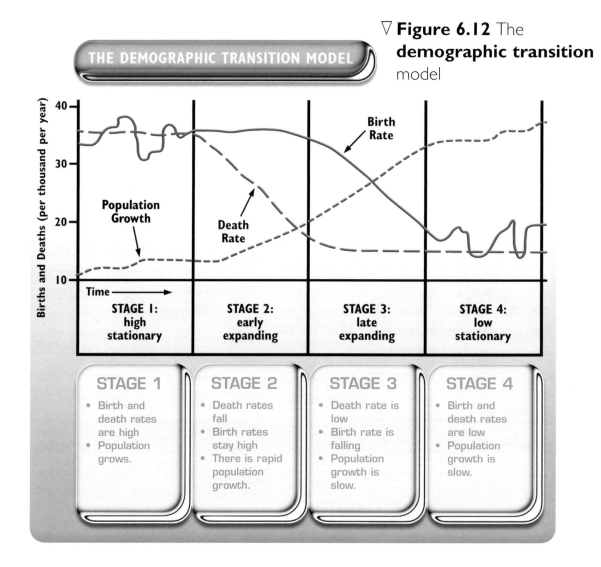

△ **Figure 6.12** The **demographic transition** model

THE DEMOGRAPHIC TRANSITION MODEL

Births and Deaths (per thousand per year)

Birth Rate

Population Growth

Death Rate

Time →

| STAGE 1: high stationary | STAGE 2: early expanding | STAGE 3: late expanding | STAGE 4: low stationary |

STAGE 1
- Birth and death rates are high
- Population grows.

STAGE 2
- Death rates fall
- Birth rates stay high
- There is rapid population growth.

STAGE 3
- Death rate is low
- Birth rate is falling
- Population growth is slow.

STAGE 4
- Birth and death rates are low
- Population growth is slow.

BONJOUR, I am ISABELLE and live in Bordeaux in France. My sister and I live with our parents. They both work all day. Most of my friends only have small families but we all have older relations still alive. I don't think that I will get any more brothers or sisters as our parents could not afford to keep us all.

HELLO, my name is ABDUL and I live in Tanzania in Africa. I have many sisters and brothers and our family grows all the time. Not as many young children die now as in the past because we have new medicines which help them to survive. Medicines also help some of the older people in the village to live longer.

HELLO, my name is RAONI. I live with my sisters and brothers in the Amazon Rainforest. Our parents say that we must all have many children when we grow up because many babies die in our village. There are hardly any old people in my family. My grandfather died last year, he was only 43 years old. We have a very large graveyard here.

HELLO, I am MARIA and I live in Brazil. I have two brothers and a sister. My parents come from a very large family, but they say it is getting too expensive to keep a large family these days. They say that modern medicines and reliable methods of birth control have helped them live longer and limit their family to a smaller but healthier one.

△ **Figure 6.13** Population change and people's lives

Activities

1 Study Figure 6.13. Each of these children lives in a country at a different stage of the population cycle. Which stage of the population cycle is each child describing?

2 Use the data in Figure 6.14 to plot a line graph to show the changes in birth and death rate since 1600.

3 On your graph write these labels to show where the following are:
• high birth rate
• low birth rate
• high death rate
• low death rate
• falling birth rate
• falling death rate.

Date	Birth Rate	Death Rate
1600	31	30
1650	29	29
1700	30	31
1750	35	30
1800	39	26
1850	34	23
1900	29	18
1950	20	14
2000	12	12

△ **Figure 6.14** The UK's changing population

What is migration?

Migration is the number of people who move into or out of a country. **Immigration** is when people move into a country. If they move out of the country, it is **emigration**.

Why do people migrate?

People move from one area to another for lots of reasons. These can be put into two groups: **Push factors**, reasons why you would not stay; and **Pull factors**, reasons for going to another place.

People move in MEDCs because of jobs and families. People in the countryside and cities have more choice where they live. People in LEDCs, especially from the countryside, move to survive. The push and pull reasons for people in MEDCs are different to those in LEDCs.

Activities

1 Make a copy of the **Venn diagram** (Figure 6.16).

a In the 'LEDC' part, write in five reasons why people move.

b In the 'MEDC' part, write in five reasons why people move.

c In the 'both' part, write in any which are common reasons.

2 Do MEDCs and LEDCs have the same or different reasons for migration?

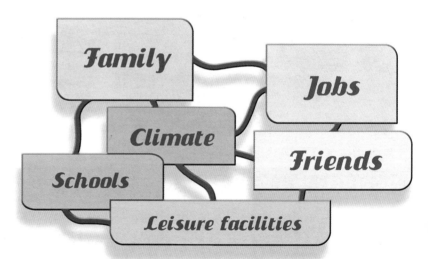

△ **Figure 6.15** Reasons why people move in MEDCs

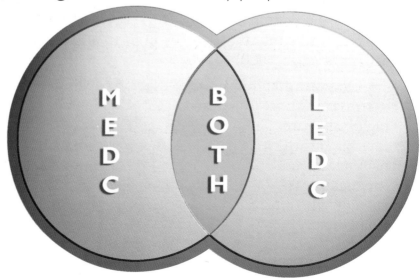

△ **Figure 6.16** Venn diagram showing Push and Pull factors in MEDCs and LEDCs

Activities

Why did Emilio Sanchez leave El Dorado?

3 Look at the statements (Figure 6.17). Why has Emilio decided to leave his village, El Dorado? Sort the statements into either Push or Pull factors.

- El Dorado once was an important farming centre.
- El Dorado has two shops that sell food and clothes.
- Emilio's family likes to watch American TV programmes.
- The USA needs farm workers.
- El Dorado's population is 175 but is getting less.
- Emilio is nearly 18 years old and has no job.
- Emilio's brothers have both left home in search of work.

- El Dorado is only 75 miles from the Mexico–USA border.
- Emilio's family earns very little money from their farm.
- Emilio's uncle works illegally in the USA. He earns 10 times what he earns in El Dorado.
- El Dorado has more old people than young ones like Emilio.
- El Dorado has a memorial to those who have died trying to cross the border.

△ **Figure 6.17** Why did Emilio Sanchez leave El Dorado?

What is migration?

The effect of migration on the migrants

People can have strong reasons for moving between countries. People will even risk their lives for the chance to live somewhere that will give them a better life.

△ **Figure 6.19** Ferry unloading at Dover (left); **Forensi**c inspecting a lorry (right)

Grim find of 58 bodies in lorry exposes smugglers' evil trade

The custom's officer was very worried. He knew that something was wrong. He opened the doors of the container. He expected the refrigerated unit to blow out cold air. Instead, the air was warm and smelt. He peered in. In the dim light he saw two Chinese men gasping for air. Behind them, he saw a nightmare. Fifty-eight bodies lay dead on the metal floor.

The routine inspection at Dover Docks discovered 56 men and 4 women. They were illegal immigrants from Fujan Province in China. They had paid a gang called the Snakeheads to bring them to Britain. The Chinese wanted the chance to start a new life in Britain.

△ **Figure 6.18** Adapted from the *Guardian*, Tuesday, 20 June, 2000

△ **Figure 6.20** The route the refugees' lorry took from China to the UK

The story of the Chinese people who tried to get into the UK illegally shows this determination (Figure 6.18). They paid a smuggling gang to take them by lorry and ferry from The Netherlands to Dover, England. The risk was too great and things went badly wrong for these people.

The effects of migration on the places people move to or from

Migrants who move into another country can change an area. This can worry some people who do not like change. Some people feel that it is unfair to change their way of life for these immigrants.

The areas from where people are moving suffer problems. These are often poor rural areas. As people leave, the villages become smaller. There are fewer young people left to continue the work and traditions of the community.

Dover, no port in a storm for refugees

Dover is facing a problem. Many of the local residents have signed a petition to stop Kent County Council adding £3 to the council tax. The Council wants the extra money to help the refugees and asylum seekers stay who arrive in Dover.

Local people like Shelia Farrell and Chris Ryan are appalled. They believe that the asylum seekers and refugees are having a bad effect on Dover. "We're trying to do something for the residents of Dover, and we get called racist".

△ **Figure 6.21** Adapted from the *Guardian*, Tuesday, 28 March, 2000

Film of the week 'Not One Less'

Peter Preston

This film is about a primary school class deep in rural China. There are no adults left to become teachers, so a 13-year-old girl, Wei, is given the job. The film tells us that a million children a year have to drop out of school in China because of poverty. It reminds us that the pull of the city is using up resources and hope from the countryside in China.

△ **Figure 6.22** From the *Observer*, Sunday, 25 June, 2000

Activities

1 Use the information on pages 116–17 to suggest how migration affects the different groups listed below.

• A young Chinese couple from rural China
• The parents of the Chinese couple
• A gang smuggling migrants into the UK
• Customs officials in Dover
• A housing estate where migrants settle.

One of the most famous mass migrations happened just over 100 years ago in the USA. The Gold Rush attracted thousands of people. It is an example of the hardships people will put up with in search of wealth.

▽ **Figure 6.23**

The Californian Gold Rush

In the summer of 1848 gold was found in California. The news spread all over America and Mexico. Newspaper stories reported men who became rich mining gold in California. That winter, people set out for California. They sold all their possessions to get there. These gold seekers were called Forty-Niners. They came from Europe, Asia and Australia.

Many Forty-Niners followed the Oregon trails across the Great Plains to reach California. Spring rains made the journey difficult. An epidemic of cholera followed the rains. This killed thousands of the migrants. By 1852 over 200 000 gold seekers had reached California.

△ **Figure 6.24** Direction of the Gold Rush

△ **Figure 6.25** A Gold Rush town

ICT links

To find out more about the Californian Gold Rush and its effect on people and the environment, take Oakland Museum's virtual tour:
www.museumca.org/goldrush/

Activities

1 Suggest three problems the Forty-Niners had during their journey to California.

2 When they got to California, they settled in 'gold-towns'. Imagine you are one of these Forty-Niners. Write a letter to your family telling them about your journey and new life in California and draw a picture of what it is like.

Many people who migrate do not have a choice. They have to leave because of wars or natural disasters, for example, famine, flooding. It could also be because of the development of natural resources, for example, a dam.

› The Narmada River Project, India

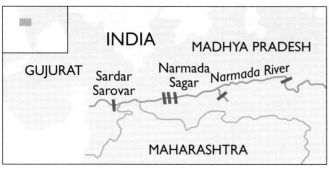

◁ **Figure 6.26** Map showing dams on the Narmada River, India

The Narmada River Project flooded many people's homes. They had to move away. Water is a precious natural resource in this dry region.

The Indian Government wants:
• water for farming
• water to produce electricity for industry
• international help to develop the region.

The Save the Narmada Movement protested. They say the project would affect 200 000 people and damage the region's fragile ecology.

Protesters say the flooding will submerge forest and farmland, disrupt fisheries and increase the risk of diseases. Some scientists have suggested that the large dams could cause earthquakes.

Supporters claim the project will supply water to 30 million people. It would water enough crops to feed 20 million people.

△ **Figure 6.27** Sardar Sarovar dam, Narmada River project

FACT FILE: NARMADA

Project began in 1979

3 200 dams to be built along 1 200 km Narmada River

Gujarat, Madhya Pradesh, Maharashtra and Rajasthan likely to benefit

Protesters say it will displace 200 000 people and damage ecology

World Bank withdrew in 1993

To be fully complete by 2025

Activities

3 How does the project affect the following people who live in the Narmada Valley:
• A village farmer?
• A landowner and farmer?
• A factory owner?

4 Design a poster that a flooded village might use for protest against the project.

5 Should people lose their homes so that natural resources are developed? Use the sentence prompts below to help you.

I think that people should/should not lose their homes.

One reason is ....

Another reason is ....

This assessment is an investigation about how people are affected by Nigeria's oil and gas industry. There is background information to use on these two pages.

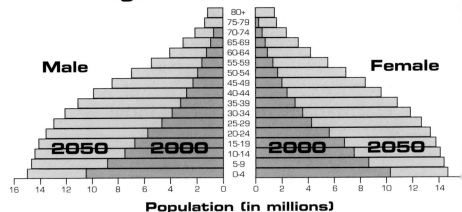

Nigeria: 2000 & 2050

Male   Female

2050   2000   2000   2050

Population (in millions)

△ **Figure 6.29** Population pyramid for Nigeria. It shows that the population of Nigeria will be much bigger in 2050. This means Nigeria will have to find more money to look after these people

Figure 6.29 shows the population pyramid for Nigeria. It has the figures for 2000 and predicts the population for 2050. Nigeria's population will increase. This will have an impact on Nigeria's economy and the quality of life for the people.

▽ **Figure 6.30** The location of Nigeria

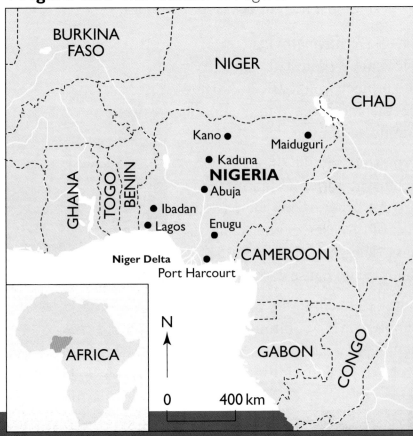

FACT FILE: NIGERIA

Nigeria is in West Africa

The area is 923 76 square km

The climate is sub-tropical

The population growth rate is high (3% per year)

The capital city is Abuja

Nigeria became independent in 1960

The official language is English

Nigeria became a democratic civilian government in May 1999.

The president is Olusegun Obasanjo

△ **Figure 6.28** Nigeria: Key Facts

▽ **Figure 6.31** From Shell Nigeria website

Major Oil Spill at Yorla Well-10

Incident

On Sunday 29th April, 2001 a local community leader reported a major oil spill at Yorla. A helicopter survey found oil and gas was spraying from the well. The well was one kilometre from the nearest community. Evidence from experts showed that sabotage caused the spill.

Immediate actions taken

- Shell Nigeria set up an emergency team to deal with the spill.
- Environment authorities were notified of the spill.
- Shell Nigeria brought in experts from the US to help control the spill.
- Shell Nigeria asked local communities to move equipment into the area.
- Local communities were provided with supplies of food and water.
- A mobile clinic provided medical help.

FACT FILE: THE NIGER DELTA

Covers 70 000 square kilometres

The world's third biggest mangrove forest

An important wildlife area

7 million people live here

Large oil reserves

94 oil fields

6 000 km of oil pipelines

Oil earns 50% of Nigeria's income

Most Nigerians are farmers

Some Nigerians are oil workers

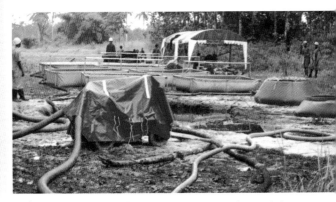

△ **Figure 6.32** Environmental problems related to the oil industry

Assessment task

Tasks

1 Use the information on pages 120–21 to write a report to the Nigerian oil industry. You can use the ICT links to find out more about Nigeria. The writing frame (Figure 6.33) will help you.

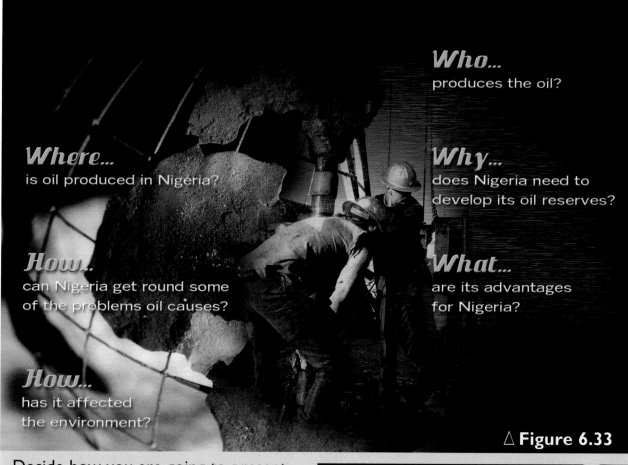

Where... is oil produced in Nigeria?

How... can Nigeria get round some of the problems oil causes?

How... has it affected the environment?

Who... produces the oil?

Why... does Nigeria need to develop its oil reserves?

What... are its advantages for Nigeria?

△ **Figure 6.33**

Decide how you are going to present your report: as a poster or as a talk. Use the questions on Figure 6.33 to help you.

ICT links

General statistics:
www.your-nation.com

Review

This chapter has been about the topic of population. Now it's time to review what you have done. Some important points are:

• People live in different places for different reasons.
• Population is unevenly distributed. There are crowded and empty areas.
• The population cycle shows how the birth and death rates change.
• A population changes as a country becomes richer and developed.
• A population pyramid is used to study a country's population.
• There are many reasons for migration, some positive, some negative.
• Migration affects the places people leave and places where they go.
• When natural resources are developed, people are affected.
• It is important to protect the environment.

Activities

1 Use Figure 6.34 to help you.
  a Use a large sheet of paper.
b Write 'population' in the middle.
c Write the ideas above around the word 'population'.
d For each idea, add an example or notes to describe what it means.
e As well as using words, draw in ideas.
f When you have completed your chart, compare it with others in your class.
g Describe one thing that you have learnt.

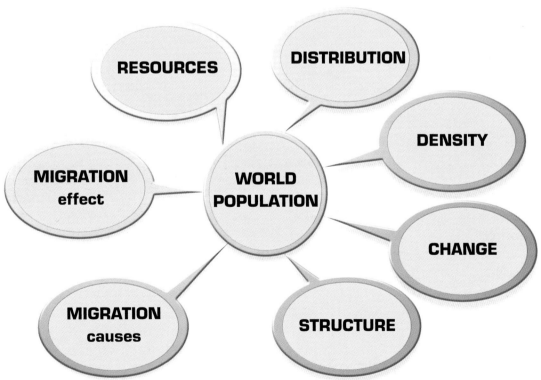

△ **Figure 6.34** Population: a summary

Glossary

Access
How easy a place is to get to.

Anemometer
A piece of equipment to measure wind speed.

Area
An amount of land.

Atmosphere
The layer of gases around the Earth.

Barometer
A piece of equipment used to measure air pressure.

Beaufort scale
A number scale used to identify different wind speeds.

Biased
A one-sided point of view.

Biome
A large-scale ecosystem with the same type of climate and vegetation.

Birth rate
The number of babies born per 1 000 people per year.

Climate
The average weather of a place.

Climate graph
A graph to show average monthly temperature and precipitation for a place.

Communications
Ways of giving and receiving information.

Community
A group of people, plants or animals having something(s) in common.

Compare
How things are the same or different.

Conflict
Where the interests of one or more groups clash.

Congested
An unusually high build up of something, e.g. traffic, people.

Continent
The largest unit of land the earth is divided into.

Death rate
The number of deaths per 1 000 people per year.

Demographic transition
A graph showing a model of the changes in a country's birth and death rates.

Derelict
Land which has fallen into disrepair.

Desert
An area which receives very little rain.

Distance
How far it is from one place to another.

Eastings
Grid lines on an OS map that run from top to bottom of the map.

Economy
An area's or country's wealth and resources.

Emigration
People moving out of a country.

Environment
The total features – living and non-living – that make up a place.

Equator
Latitude 0 degrees – an imaginary line which divides the Earth into the northern and southern hemispheres.

Field sketch
A sketch drawn outside the classroom looking at a real landscape.

Fieldwork
Finding out about a place by visiting it.

Finite
A limited resource, one that will run out, e.g. oil.

Flash floods
A flood that happens quickly and without warning.

Forensics
Scientists who carry out legal investigations.

Front
Where cold and warm air meet.

Frontal rain
Rain caused by warm air rising up over cold air and condensing.

Geographical enquiry
A sequence of geographical questions.

Global Positioning System
The use of satellites and receivers to locate places.

Globe
A round shape that represents the earth.

Greenwich meridian
Longitude 0 degrees.

Grid reference
A way of using numbers or letters to locate places on maps.

Honeypot site
A popular tourist location which attracts many visitors.

Human geography
Features that have been built by people.

Immigration
People moving into a country.

Industrial inertia
The tendency for an industry to remain in a particular place even though the original reasons for that choice are no longer as important.

Informal economy
Casual, irregular work, e.g. street-selling.

International
From places in other countries.

Land use
What people build on and do with the land.

Landscape
What an area of land looks like.

Latitude
Numbered lines on the globe that are parallel to each other from east to west.

LEDCs
Less Economically Developed Countries: the poorer countries of mainly South America, Africa and Asia.

Line drawing
A simple sketch with lines and some labels and notes.

Local area
The area within a few kilometres of where you live.

Location
The place where something is found.

Longitude
Numbered lines on the globe that run from the North Pole to the South Pole.

Map projection
How a map is drawn so that a curved surface can be shown on a flat sheet of paper.

Maritime
Influenced by the sea.

MEDCs
More Economically Developed Countries: the richer countries of mainly North America and Europe.

Meteorological
Relating to the study of conditions in the atmosphere to forecast weather.

Meteorologist
A person who studies the weather.

Microclimates
The climate of a small area caused by local factors.

Migration
People moving from one place to live in another.

Minimum–Maximum thermometer
A piece of weather equipment which can measure the highest and lowest temperatures in 24 hours.

National
To do with a country.

National Park
An area of outstanding natural beauty, protected by law and managed by Park authorities to conserve the environment for future generations.

Nomad
A people who live in mainly desert areas but are not permanently settled in one place.

Northings
Lines on an OS map that cross from side to side.

Ordnance Survey
The organisation responsible for drawing the main maps of the UK.

Pedestrian
Travelling on foot.

Physical geography
The natural features of a place, such as hills.

Population cycle
see **demographic transition**

Population density
The number of people living in a given area.

Population distribution
The pattern of where people live.

Population growth rate
The amount a country's population increases each year.

Population pyramid
A graph showing the structure of a country's population.

Population structure
The way a country's population is split between males and females of different ages.

Precipitation
Water which falls from the sky in liquid or solid form, e.g. rain, hail, sleet, snow.

Prevailing wind
The most common direction the wind blows from.

Primary industry
Extracting raw materials from the land or sea.

Public park
A recreation area in a settlement.

Pull factors
The things which attract someone to migrate to a place.

Push factors
The things which force someone out of a place.

Quaternary industry
Managing information and/or using information technology.

Rain gauge
A piece of weather equipment to measure the amount of rainfall.

Redevelop
Redesign and/or rebuild an area.

Regeneration
Bringing a run-down area back to life, improving it.

Regional
A large area that, in the UK, consists of several counties.

Relief rain
Rain caused by air being forced to move over upland areas, e.g. hills.

Reservoir
A purpose-built lake to store water.

Rural
To do with the countryside.

Sanitary facilities
Baths and showers.

Scale
The amount by which real places are reduced so that a map can be drawn.

Sea currents
Layers of warm and cold water moving through the sea.

Secondary industry
Processing raw materials into manufactured products.

Services
Facilities, e.g. shops that people can use.

Stevenson screen
A box used to hold and protect weather equipment.

Subsistence farms
Farms that grow food mainly for the family to eat.

Synoptic code
Symbols used to show the weather recorded at weather stations.

Temperate climate
A mild climate.

Temperature range
The difference between the hottest and coldest temperatures over a period of time.

Tertiary industry
Providing a service either for an individual customer or a company.

Theme park
A recreation area which has rides and other attractions.

Thermometer
A piece of weather equipment used to measure the temperature.

Transnational companies
Large companies operating in more than one country.

Tube wells
Long hollow holes to allow people to get water from deep below the soil.

Urban
A built-up area, e.g. a city.

Values
A point of view. What people believe.

Venn diagram
A diagram showing relationship by overlapping circles.

Vertical air photo
A photograph taken looking directly down on the land.

Weather
The day-to-day changes in the atmosphere.

Wind rose
A diagram used to plot wind direction.

Wind vane
A piece of weather equipment to find the direction of the wind.

World Heritage sites
Through the United Nations, internationally agreed sites of historic, wildlife, cultural and natural value.

Index